TRISTAN
AND ISOLDA

Opera in Three Acts

By

RICHARD WAGNER

Vocal Score by
RICHARD KLEINMICHEL

English Version by
HENRY GRAFTON CHAPMAN

With an Essay on the
Story of the Opera by
H. E. KREHBIEL

Ed. 619

G. SCHIRMER   *New York / London*

Printed in the U. S. A.

TRISTAN AND ISOLDA
DRAMA IN THREE ACTS

CHARACTERS

TRISTAN	*Tenor*	MELOT	*Tenor*
KING MARK	*Bass*	BRANGÆNA	*Soprano*
ISOLDA	*Soprano*	A SHEPHERD	*Tenor*
KURVENAL	*Baritone*	A HELMSMAN	*Baritone*

SAILORS, KNIGHTS AND ATTENDANTS

SCENE OF ACTION

Act I. At sea on the deck of Tristan's ship, on the voyage from Ireland to Cornwall.

Act II. King Mark's castle in Cornwall.

Act III. Tristan's castle in Brittany.

. .

*The drama was first performed at Munich on June 10, 1865
with the following cast:*

TRISTAN	*Herr Schnorr von Carolsfeld*
ISOLDE	*Frau Schnorr von Carolsfeld*
KÖNIG MARKE	*Herr Zottmayer*
KURWENAL	*Herr Mitterwurzer*
MELOT	*Herr Heinrich*
BRANGÄNE	*Frl. Deinet*
EIN HIRT	*Herr Simons*
EIN STEUERMANN	*Herr Hartmann*

TRISTAN AND ISOLDA

"A VASSAL is sent to woo a beauteous princess for his lord. While he is bringing her home the two, by accident, drink a love-potion, and ever thereafter their hearts are fettered together. In the mid-day of delirious joy, in the midnight of deepest woe, and through all the emotional hours between, their thoughts are only of each other, for each other. Meanwhile the princess has become the vassal's queen. Then the wicked love of the pair is discovered, and the knight is obliged to seek safety in a foreign land. There (strange note this to our ears) he marries another princess, whose name is like that of his love, save for the addition 'With the White Hand;' but when wounded unto death he sends across the water for her who is still his true love, that she come and be his healer. The ship which is sent to bring her is to bear white sails on its return if successful in the mission; black, if not. Day after day the knight waits for the coming of his love, while the lamp of his life burns lower and lower. At length the sails of the ship appear on the distant horizon. The knight is now himself too weak to look. 'White or black?' he asks of his wife. 'Black,' replies she, jealousy prompting the falsehood; and the knight's heart-strings snap in twain just as his love steps over the threshold of the chamber. Oh, the pity of it! for with the lady is her lord, who, having learned the story of the fateful potion, has come to unite the lovers. Then the queen, too, dies, and the remorseful king buries the lovers in a common grave, from whose caressing sod spring a rose-bush and a vine and intertwine so curiously that none may separate them."* Thus, in simplest outline, runs the legend which Wagner has given dramatic form in his "Tristan und Isolde." It was long in the poet-composer's mind before it took shape. Wagner was an omnivorous reader; but it was during the period of his activity as operatic conductor in Dresden, from 1843 to 1849, that he gave particular attention to the study of old Germanic legends. How these studies bore fruit in "Lohengrin," "Tannhäuser," "Wieland der Schmiedt" (which remained a sketch), "Siegfried's Tod" (which grew into "Götterdämmerung" and eventually into the Nibelung trilogy), and "Parsifal," the world knows. The legend of Tristram (or Tristan, to adopt the German appellation) is of vast antiquity; its origin is lost in the mists of early civilizations, like those of its companions which tell of Siegfried and Parsifal, with which it has elements in common and which had loving communion in Wagner's mind. As we know it, the tale of Tristan is Keltic, and it is at least remotely possible that the original Aryan root first blossomed in modern

---

* "*Studies in the Wagnerian Drama*," by H. E. Krehbiel.

18325   (v)

literary form in Wales. This was the fond belief of Sir Walter Scott, who in 1804 edited a metrical version attributed to Thomas the Rhymer, who was supposed to have been a poet of the fourteenth century. This branch of curious and interesting inquiry does not necessarily call for attention here, however, since the source followed by Wagner is sufficiently obvious. Enough that the singular charm of the tale "which half a millennium of poets have celebrated as the High Song of Love, the Canticle of all Canticles which hymn the universal passion" (*op. cit.*), is alike familiar to English and German literature. It has been told by Sir Thomas Malory, Lord Tennyson, Matthew Arnold, and Algernon Swinburne, each of whom has placed the stamp of his peculiar genius upon it. Long ago the love-song was sung by the French trouvères, and after them by the German Minnesinger. The most famous mediæval version is the German epic of Gottfried von Strassburg, a translation of which into the modern language by Hermann Kurtz was published in 1844. This, it may safely be assumed, fell under the eye of Wagner while he was delving in the legendary lore of his people in the Dresden period. Gottfried left the story unfinished, but two poets of his century, the thirteenth, were his continuators. Following these — Ulrich von Türnheim and Heinrich von Freiberg — Kurtz wrote the dénouement indicated in our outline, namely, the life of the hero in Brittany with Isolde of the White Hand, and his death as the immediate result of the falsehood about the sails. While Wagner was sketching his drama in 1855 an edition of Gottfried's epic appeared under the editorship of Karl Simrock. It offered nothing new in the reading of the text, but there were some ingenious allusions in the preface which seem to have provided Wagner with some of the pictures and symbolism with which the second act of his tragedy is rife. These were the dawn of day during the lovers' meeting (of which Shakespeare made such exquisite use in "Romeo and Juliet"), and the fateful result of the extinguishment of the torch, which has a prototype in the ancient legend of Hero and Leander. The incident of the sails belongs to Greek story — the legend of Ægeus and Theseus. Wagner evidently intended to employ the incident in a changed form, turning the black sails into a black flag, for, writing to Liszt late in 1854, he said: "As I have never in my life enjoyed the true felicity of love, I shall erect to this most beautiful of my dreams [he refers to the Siegfried drama] a monument in which, from beginning to end, this love shall find fullest gratification. I have sketched in my head a 'Tristan und Isolde,' the simplest of musical conceptions, but full-blooded; with the 'black flag' which waves at the end I shall then cover myself — to die." Other significant departures from the old legend made by Wagner, obviously for the purpose of intensifying and ennobling the character and passion of the fabled lovers, are the omission of the element of accident in the drinking of the potion, and the second Isolde. Concerning the first of these I have spoken at considerable length in the book quoted at the beginning of this preface, and, since it is a matter that goes deep into the ethics of the drama, I may, perhaps, be pardoned for repeating some of my words: "The versions of Gottfried von Strassburg, Matthew Arnold, Swinburne, Tennyson and Wagner present three points of view from which the love of the tragic pair must be studied. With the first three the drinking is purely accidental, and the passion which leads to the destruction of the lovers is something for which they are in no wise responsible. With Tennyson there is no philtre, and the passion is all guilty. With Wagner the love exists before the dreadful drinking, and the potion is less a maker of uncontrollable passion than a drink which causes the lovers to forget duty, honor and the respect due to the laws of society. It is a favorite idea of Wagner's that the hero of tragedy should be a type of humanity freed from all bonds of conventionality. It is unquestionable, in my mind, that in his scheme we are to accept the love-potion as merely the agency with which Wagner struck from his hero the shackles of convention. Unquestionably, as Bayard Taylor argued, the love-draught is the Fate of the Tristan drama, and this brings into notice the significance of Wagner's chief variation. It is an old theory, too often overlooked now, that there must be at least a taint of guilt in the conduct of a tragic hero in order that the feeling of pity excited by his sufferings may not overcome the idea of justice in the catastrophe. This theory was plainly an outgrowth of the deep religious purpose of the Greek tragedy. Wagner puts antecedent and conscious guilt at the door of both of his heroic characters. They love before the philtre, and do not pay the reverence to the passion which, in the highest conception, it commands. Tristan is carried away by love of power and glory before men, and himself suggests and compels by his threats Marke's marriage, which is a crime against the love which he bears Isolde and she bears him. There is guilt enough in Isolde's determination and effort to commit murder and suicide. Thus Wagner presents us the idea of Fate in the latest and highest aspect that it assumed in the minds of the Greek poets, and he arouses our pity and our horror, not only by the sufferings of the principals, but also by making an innocent and amiable prompting to underlie the action which brings down the catastrophe. It is Brangäne's love for her mistress that persuades her to shield her from the crime of murder and protect her life. From whatever point of view the question is treated, it seems to me that Wagner's variation is an improvement on the old legends, and that the objection, which German critics have urged, that the love of the pair is merely a chemical product, and so outside of human sympathy, falls to the ground."

The letter to Liszt from which a brief quotation has been made indicates that "Tristan und Isolde" had its inception in Wagner's mind in the fall of 1854. He was then living in Zurich, and it was three years before he began the execution of his plan. It was not to be a monument to a dream of felicity never experienced, or to his despair at ever seeing the completion of his "Siegfried" drama (which had advanced to the second act when it was laid aside), but the tribute to a consuming passion for the wife of a benefactor, whose generosity provided him with an idyllic home at Triebschen on the shores of Lake Lucerne. Love for Mathilde Wesendonck was the inspiration of both book and score, and it speaks tumultuously and with unexampled eloquence in the love music of the second act. Not until Wagner's letters to the lady were published, long years after both were dead, were all the facts in the case known. Frau Wesendonck was the author of the "Fünf Gedichte" which owe their preservation to the music to which Wagner wedded them. Two of the songs, "Im Treibhaus" and "Träume," when published were described as "Studies for Tristan und Isolde," and the latter at least may be set down as having, in a special sense, an autobiographical value. Four of the five were composed in the winter of 1857–58; "Im Treibhaus" on May 1, 1858. The theme of "Träume" was the germ of the love music of the second act of the tragedy, that of "Im Treibhaus" of the prelude to the third act. The prose scenario of the drama was written in August, 1857, finding its completion on the 20th day of that month, and the poem was practically finished within a month thereafter, that is to say, by September 18th. The pencil sketches of the music, all painstakingly and lovingly written over in ink by Frau Wesendonck, to whom they were presented by the composer, bear dates as follows: Act I, October 1, 1857, to New Year's eve; Act II, May 4 to July 1, 1858; Act III, April 9 to July 16, 1859. So much for what may be called the inner, or psychological, history of the work; its outward story is more prosaic. In May, 1857, after Wagner had been eight years an exile from his native land, he received an invitation from Dom Pedro, Emperor of Brazil, to write an opera for Rio de Janeiro, come to the Brazilian capital, and conduct its first performances. It does not appear that Wagner ever seriously contemplated accepting the invitation, but it set him to thinking, and may have been the jolt which turned his mind again to the project which he had announced to Liszt two and a half years previously. Years had passed since he had begun work on "Der Ring des Nibelungen," and that stupendous enterprise held out little promise of fruition in the way of publication, and less of performance and royalties. At any rate he formulated a plan to write the opera in German, have it translated into Italian, dedicate the score to the Emperor of Brazil, and permit the performance in Rio de Janeiro, utilizing the occasion, if possible, to secure a performance of "Tannhäuser" beforehand. Meanwhile he would have the opera produced in its original tongue at Strass-

(viii)

burg, then a French city conveniently near the German border, with Niemann in the titular rôle and an orchestra from Karlsruhe, or some other German city containing an opera-house. Of course, he communicated the plan to Liszt at once, and equally of course, Liszt approved the project heartily, though he was greatly amazed at the intelligence which he had from another source that Wagner intended to write the music with an eye to a performance in Italian. "How in the name of all the gods are you going to make of it an opera for Italian singers, as B. tells me you are? Well, since the incredible and impossible have become your elements, perhaps you will achieve this too;" and he promised to go to Strassburg with the Wagnerian coterie as a guard of honor for the composer. Nothing came of either plan, as we shall see, but Wagner, under a vastly different stimulus, wrote the opera, doing much of the work in Venice, whither he went that he might have quiet and work undisturbedly. He had carried on fruitless negotiations with Breitkopf & Härtel for the publication of his "Ring des Nibelungen," but the new opera seemed like a more practical proposition to the publishers, and they agreed to take the score for the equivalent of $800, which sum they were to pay him on the receipt of the first act. When the project of the German performance was revived, Eduard Devrient, director of the Grand Ducal Theatre at Karlsruhe, persuaded the composer to give up Strassburg in favor of his city, which, in Schnorr von Carolsfeld and his wife, contained two artists in every way adapted to create the hero and heroine of the tragedy. Wagner wanted to supervise the production, however, and this was impossible so long as the decree of banishment for his political offences in Saxony was still in force. The Grand Duke of Baden appealed in his behalf to the King of Saxony, but all in vain; and in the fall of 1859 Wagner went to Paris, cherishing a dream of a performance there with German singers. This project, too, failed, and Wagner found that all that was left for him to do in the way of propagandism for his art was to give some concerts in Paris and Brussels, and finally, in 1861, to give the performances at the Grand Opera which resulted in one of the most famous and disgraceful scandals in musical history, a scandal compared with which the *guerre des buffons* and the combat of Gluckists and Piccinnists in the same city a century earlier was as child's play. Again began the search for a city in which "Tristan" might have its first hearing. Weimar, Prague, and Hanover were canvassed, and in the end Wagner turned to Vienna. Two years had elapsed since the score had been completed, and Wagner was consumed with desire to hear it, and as positive as he was of his own existence (so he writes to Ferdinand Praeger) that it was without an equal in all the world's library of music. To Vienna he now went, arriving there in May, 1861. He did not get his heart's desire, but he heard his "Lohengrin" for the first time—"Lohengrin," which had been composed thirteen years before. As for "Tristan," it was accepted for performance at the Court Opera after some delay, and rehearsals begun; but after fifty-four of these, between November, 1862, and March, 1863, it was abandoned as "impossible." The next year saw the turning-point in Wagner's career: Ludwig of Bavaria became his friend and patron. Wagner went to Munich, and within a few months it was arranged that "Tristan und Isolde" should be performed at the Royal Court Theatre. On April 18, 1865, a public invitation went out from Wagner through the columns of a Viennese newspaper to his friends to attend the projected performance. Schnorr von Carolsfeld and his wife were brought from Dresden, whither they had gone from Karlsruhe, to create the principal characters; the composer's friends, official and unofficial, foregathered in large numbers, and after several trying postponements the first performance took place under the direction of Hans von Bülow, who had made the pianoforte score of the work, on June 10, 1865. The principal parts were distributed as follows: *Tristan*, Ludwig Schnorr von Carolsfeld; *Kurwenal*, Mitterwurzer; *Melot*, Heinrich; *König Marke*, Zottmayer; *Isolde*, Frau Schnorr von Carolsfeld; *Brangäne*, Fräulein Deinet. Twenty-one-and-a-half years later the tragedy reached New York, when it had its performance on December 1, 1886, with Albert Niemann, whom the composer had chosen to be the original creator of his hero in Strassburg, as *Tristan*, and Anton Seidl, the composer's pupil and apostle, in the conductor's chair. The parts were distributed as follows: *Isolde*, Fräulein Lilli Lehmann; *Brangäne*, Marianne Brandt; *Tristan*, Albert Niemann; *Kurwenal*, Adolf Robinson; *König Marke*, Emil Fischer; *Melot*, Rudolph von Milde; *Ein Hirt*, Otto Kemlitz; *Ein Steuermann*, Emil Saenger; *Ein Seemann*, Max Alvary.

Act I. The scene is laid on board of a ship which is within a short sail of Cornwall. Thither *Tristan* is bearing *Isolde*, daughter of the Queen of Ireland, to be the wife of *Marke*, King of Cornwall. A sailor, hidden in the rigging, sings a song to his Irish sweetheart which sets loose a tempest in the heart of the princess. In an outburst of rage she declares to her maid, *Brangäne*, that she will never set foot on Cornwall's shore; she deplores the impotency of her mother's sorcery over the wind and waves which she vainly invokes to dash the ship to pieces. *Brangäne* pleads to know the cause of her mistress's tumultuous disquiet and learns of the incidents which antedate those of which she is a present witness. Disguised as a harper and calling himself Tantris, *Tristan* had come to Ireland to be healed of a wound received in battle with Morold, Isolde's betrothed, whom he had killed and thus freed Cornwall from tribute to Ireland. *Isolde* nursed the stranger, but while doing so discovered one day that the edge of his sword was broken and that a splinter of steel taken from the head of her dead lover fitted into the nick in the sword's edge. Before her, at her mercy, lay the slayer of him who was to have been her husband. She raised the sword to deal the avenging blow, but before it could descend the knight turned his glance upon her. Not upon the threatening sword, but into her eyes did he look, and in a flash her heart was empty of hate; an overwhelming love for him gushed up within her. "After telling this tale to *Brangäne*, Isolde sends the maid to summon *Tristan* to her presence; but the knight refuses to leave the helm until he has brought the ship into harbor, and his squire, *Kurwenal*, incensed at the tone addressed by the princess to one who, in his eyes, is the greatest of heroes, as answer to the summons sings a stave of a popular ballad which recounts the killing of Morold and the liberation of Cornwall by his master. The refusal completes the desperation of *Isolde*. Outraged love, injured personal and national pride (for she imagines that he who had relieved Cornwall from tribute to Ireland was now gratifying his ambition by bringing her as Ireland's tribute to Cornwall), detestation of a loveless marriage to 'Cornwall's weary king'—a thousand fierce but indefinable emotions are seething in her heart. She resolves to die, and to drag *Tristan* down to death with her. *Brangäne* unwittingly shows the way. She tries to quiet her mistress's fears of the dangers of a loveless marriage by telling her of a magic potion brewed by the queen-mother, with which she will firmly attach *Marke* to his bride. Thus innocently she takes the first step towards precipitating the catastrophe. *Isolde* demands to see the casket of magic philtres, and finds that it also contains a deadly poison. *Kurwenal* enters to announce that the ship is in the harbor and *Tristan* desires her to prepare for the landing. *Isolde* sends back greetings and a message that before she will permit the knight to escort her before the king he must obtain from her forgiveness for unforgiven guilt. Tristan obeys this second summons, and in justification of his conduct in keeping himself aloof during the voyage he, with great dignity, pleads his duty towards good morals, custom and his king. *Isolde* reminds him of the wrong done her in the slaying of her lover and her right to the vengeance which once she had renounced. *Tristan* yields the right, and offers his sword and breast, but *Isolde* replies that she cannot appear before *King Marke* as the slayer of his foremost knight, and proposes that he drink a cup of reconciliation. *Tristan* sees one-half her purpose and chivalrously consents to pledge her in what he knows to be poison. *Isolde* calls for the cup, which she had commanded *Brangäne* to prepare, and when *Tristan* has drunk part of its contents she wrenches it from his hand and drains it to the bottom. Thus they meet their doom, which is not death and surcease of sorrow, but life and misery; for *Brangäne* had disobeyed her mistress out of love, and mixed a love-potion instead of a death-draught. A moment of bewilderment, and the two fated ones are in each other's arms, pouring out an ecstasy of passion; then the maids of honor robe *Isolde* to receive *King Marke*, who is coming on board to greet his bride."

Act II. Scene, a garden before *Queen Isolde's* chamber; time, a lovely night in summer. A torch burns in a ring beside the door leading from the chamber into the garden. The king has gone a-hunting, and the tones of his hunting-horns, answering each other, come floating on the night air. *Isolde* appears with *Brangäne* and pleads with her to extinguish the torch, thus giving a preconcerted signal to *Tristan*, who is waiting in concealment. "But *Brangäne* suspects treachery on the part of *Melot*, a knight who is jealous of *Tristan* and himself enamoured of *Isolde*, and who had planned the nocturnal hunt. She warns her mistress and begs her to wait. In their dialogue there is lovely fencing with the incident of the vanishing sounds of the hunt, like Shakespeare's dalliance with nightingale and lark in 'Romeo and Juliet.' To *Isolde* the horns are but the rustling of the forest leaves as they are caressed by the wind, or the purling and laughing of the brook. Longing has eaten up all patience, all discretion, all fear. She extinguishes the torch in spite of *Brangäne's* pleadings, and with wildly-waving scarf beckons on her hurrying lover. Beneath the foliage they sing their love through all the gamut of hope and despair." There is a rude interruption in the moment of their supremest ecstasy. *Kurwenal* dashes on the scene with sword drawn and a shout: "Save thyself, Tristan!" *King Marke*, his courtiers, and *Melot*, are at his heels. The aged king accuses his nephew and knight of treachery and bemoans his ingratitude and the loss of his love. From the words of the heart-torn king we learn that he had been forced into the marriage with *Isolde* by the disturbed state of his kingdom, and that he had not consented to it until *Tristan* (whose purpose it was to quiet the jealous anger of the Cornish barons) had threatened to depart from Cornwall unless the King revoked his decision to make him his successor. Tristan's answer to *Marke's* sorrowful upbraidings is to obtain a promise from *Isolde* that she will follow him into the "wondrous realm of night." Then he makes a feint of attacking *Melot*, but permits the traitor's sword to reach his side. He falls wounded unto death.

Act III. "The dignified, reserved knight of the first act, the impassioned lover of the second, is now a dream-haunted, longing, despairing, dying man, lying under a lime-tree in the yard of his ancestral castle in Brittany, wasting his last bit of strength in feverish fancies and ardent longings touching *Isolde. Kurwenal* has sent for her. Will she come? A shepherd tells of vain watches for the sight of a sail by playing a mournful melody on his pipe. Oh, the heart-hunger of the hero! The longing! Will she never come? The fever is consuming him, and his heated brain breeds fancies which one moment lift him above all memories of pain, and the next bring him to the verge of madness. Cooling breezes waft him again towards Ireland, whose princess healed the wound struck by Morold, then ripped it up again with the avenging sword with its telltale nick. From her hands he took the drink whose poison sears his heart. Accursed the cup and accursed the hand that brewed it! Will the shepherd never change his doleful strain? Ah, *Isolde*, how beautiful you are! The ship, the ship! It must be in sight. *Kurwenal*, have you no eyes? *Isolde's* ship! A merry tune bursts from the shepherd's pipe. It is the ship! What flag flies at the peak? The flag of 'All 's well!' Now the ship disappears behind a cliff. There the breakers are treacherous. Who is at the helm? Friend or foe? *Melot's* accomplice? Are you, too, a traitor, *Kurwenal? Tristan's* strength is unequal to the excitement of the moment. His mind becomes dazed. He hears *Isolde's* voice, and his wandering fancy transforms it into the torch whose extinction once summoned him to her side: '*Do I hear* the light?' He staggers to his feet and tears the bandages from his wound. 'Ha! my blood! flow merrily now! She who opened the wound is here to heal it!' Life endures but for one embrace, one glance, one word: 'Isolde!' While *Isolde* lies mortally stricken upon *Tristan's* corpse, *Marke* and his train arrive upon a second ship. *Brangäne* has told the secret of the love-draught, and the king has come to unite the lovers. But his purpose is not known, and faithful *Kurwenal* receives his death-blow while trying to hold the castle against *Marke's* men. He dies at *Tristan's* side. *Isolde*, unconscious of all these happenings, sings out her broken heart and expires.

> "'*And ere her ear might hear, her heart had heard,*
> *Nor sought she sign for witness of the word;*
> *But came and stood above him, newly dead,*
> *And felt his death upon her: and her head*
> *Bowed, as to reach the spring that slakes all drought;*
> *And their four lips became one silent mouth.*'"

H. E. KREHBIEL

Blue Hill, Maine, September 18, 1906.

ORDER OF THE SCENES

ACT I

ACT II

ACT III

TRISTAN AND ISOLDA

Tristan and Isolda.

Act I.

Introduction.

Richard Wagner.

18325

espress.
cresc.
zart
dolce
ten.
belebt
animato
dim.
Belebend.
Animando.
cresc.
molto cresc.
rallent.
a tempo
zart
dolce
dim.
dim.
cresc.
cresc.

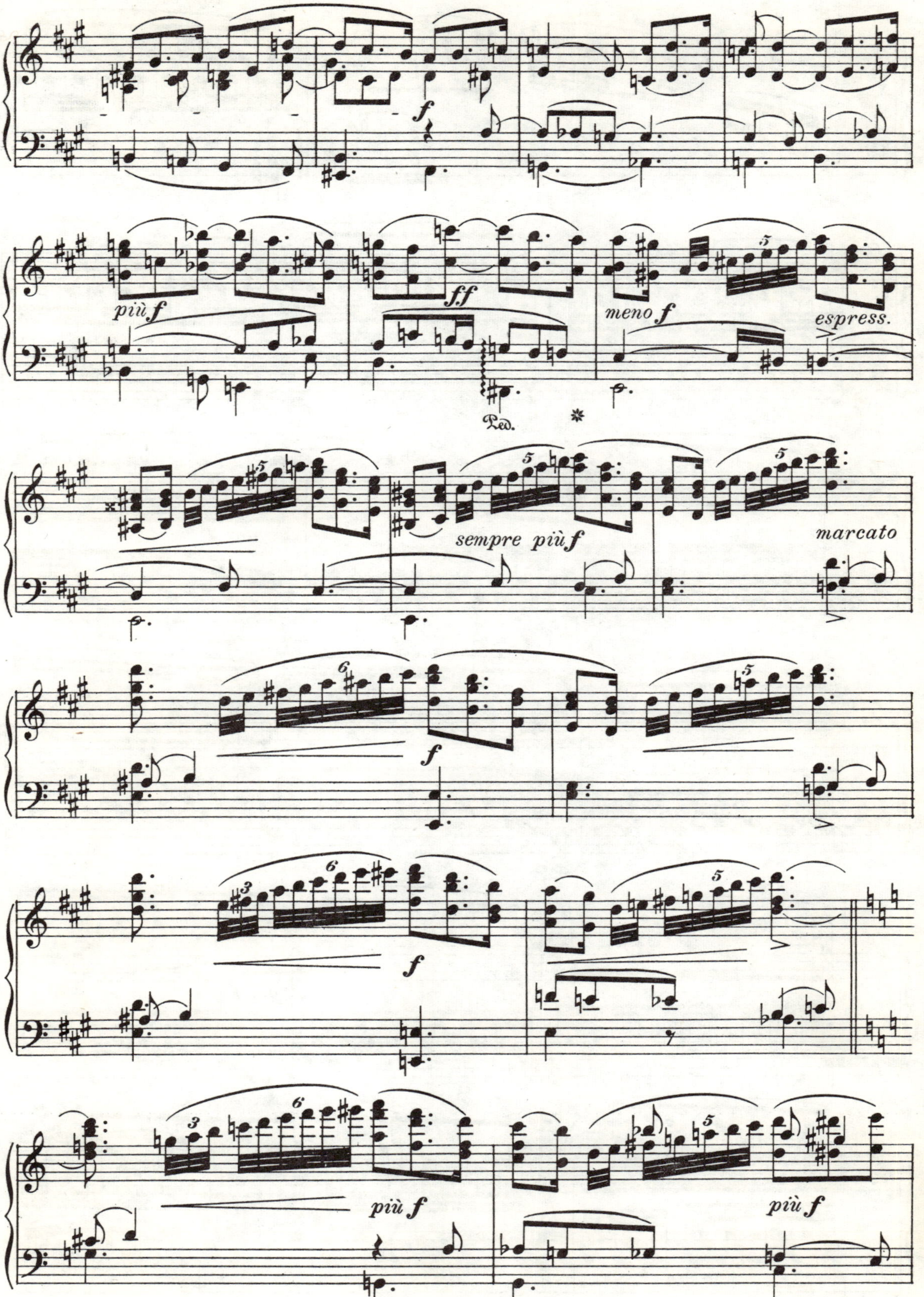
f
più f
ff
meno f
espress.
Ped.
sempre più f
marcato
f
f
più f
più f

4

Allmählich im Zeitmass etwas zurückhaltend.
Il tempo poco a poco ritenuto.

espress.

dim.

zart
dolce

cresc.

(The Curtain rises)

Scene I.

A marquee, richly hung with rugs, on the forward deck of a sailing-ship, at first entirely closed at the back; on one side a narrow companion-way leads to the cabin below.

Isolda on a couch, her head buried in the cushions. Brangæna, holding back a curtain, looks out over the side of the ship.

Mässig langsam.
Andante moderato.

The Voice of a young Sailor (from above, as if from the mast-head)   (kräftig) (energico)

Tenor.

West-wärts   schweift der Blick, ostwärts streicht das Schiff. Frisch
West-ward   glanc - es sweep, east-ward steers the ship. The

(nachlassend) (calando)

weht der Wind der Hei-math zu:_ mein i-risch Kind, wo wei-lest du?
west-wind wild blows homeward now:_ mine I-rish child, where ling'rest thou?

(etwas gedehnt) (poco steso)

Sind's dei-ner Seuf-zer We-hen, die mir die Se-gel blä-hen?_
Or is it, thou art try-ing to fill the sails, by sigh-ing?_

We-he, we-he, du Wind!_ Weh, ach we-he, mein Kind!_
Blow then, wind fresh and wild!_ Woe, ah! woe is my child!_

(feurig)
f (con fuoco)

I-ri-sche Maid,_____ du wil-de, min-ni-ge
Mine I-rish maid,_____ my wild and am-o-rous

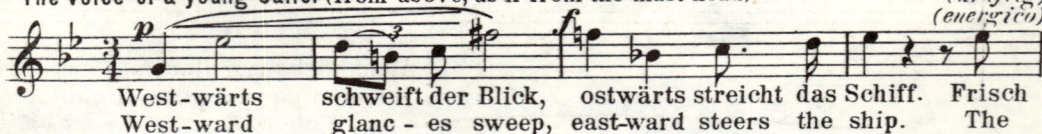

Lebhaft.
Vivace.

Isolda (starting up quickly)   (She looks round disturbed)

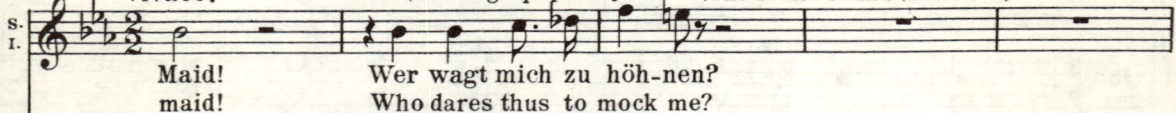

Maid!   Wer wagt mich zu höh-nen?
maid!   Who dares thus to mock me?

Mässig.
Moderato.

Brangä-ne, du?_   Sag', wo sind wir?
Brangæ-na, ho!   Say, where are we?

Brangæna (at the opening)

Blau-e Strei-fen stie-gen im
Bands of pur-ple rise in the

We-sten auf; sanft und schnell se-gelt das Schiff; auf
west-ern sky; soft and swift forg-es the ship; and

ru-hi-ger See vor A-bend-er-rei-chen wir si-cher das
holds it out calm, ere eve-ning we'll reach of a sure-ty the

Isolda. Schnell. Presto.
Welches Land? Nim-mermehr! Nicht heut', noch
What land? Nev-ermore! To-day or

Land. Kornwalls grü-nen Strand.
land. Cornwall's grass-y strand.

p f

Brangæna (lets fall the curtain and hurries anxiously to Isolda)

mor - gen! Was hör' ich! Her - rin! Ha!
ev - er! What say'st thou, Mis - tress? Oh!

Isolda (with wild gaze)

Ent-ar - tet Ge-schlecht, un - werth der Ah - nen!
De-gen - er-ate child, shame of thy fore - bears!

Wo-hin, Mut - ter, ver-gabst du die
To whom, Moth - er, hast giv - en thy

Macht, ü-ber Meer und Sturm zu ge-bie - ten?
pow'r to command the storm and the o - - cean?

O zah - me Kunst der Zau - be-rin,
O pet - ty craft! a sor - cer-ess

die nur Bal - - sam-trän - ke noch braut!
that can brew herb - po - tions a - lone!

Er-wa - che mir wie - der, küh - ne Ge - walt; herauf
A-wak - en with - in me, Spir - it of might! A-rise

— aus dem Bu - - sen, wo du dich bargst!
— in my bo - - - som, where now thou lurk'st!

Hört mei - nen Wil - - len, za - gende
Hear ye my or - - ders, cow - - er-ing

Win - de! Her - an zu Kampf und Wet - - ter-ge-
breez - es! Up! up! and charge, with shock of the

tös', zu to-ben-der Stür-me wü-then-dem Wir-bel!
storm, and roar of the tem-pest_thun-der-ing whirl-winds!

Treibt aus dem Schlaf dies träu-men-de Meer,
Rouse from its sleep this slum-ber-ing sea,

weckt aus dem Grund seine grol-len-de Gier! Zeigt ihm die Beu-te,
wak-en the deep and the growl of its greed! Show it the boo-ty,

die ich ihm bie-te! Zerschlag'
I bring to bait it! And shat-

_es dies trot-zi-ge Schiff, des zer-schell-ten Trümmer ver-
_ter this in-so-lent ship, o-ver-whelm and tear it to

I.

schling's! / shreds!

Und was auf ihm / And what there-on

ff   *dim.*

I.

lebt, den we-henden A-them, den lass' ich euch Win - den zum / lives, their trem-u-lous life-breath, I leave to you winds for a

p   *f*   *f*

Brangæna (in great alarm and anxiety for Isolda)

I.
B.

Lohn! O weh! Ach! Ach des Ü-bels, das ich ge- / wage! Ah woe! Ah! Ah! This trouble long have I

ff   *ff*   *dim.*

B.

ahnt!_ I - sol - de! Her - rin! Theu - res Herz! Was / feared!_ I - sol - da! La - dy! Dear - est heart! What

p   *cresc.* - - -

Allmählich etwas mässiger im Zeitmass.
Poco a poco più moderato.

B.

bargst du mir so lang? Nicht ei-ne Thrä - ne wein-test du Va-ter und / keep'st thou hid so long? No tear at part - ing gav - est thou fa-ther or

f   *f*   *dim.*   *p*

Mut - ter; kaum ei - nen Gruss den Blei - ben-den bo - test
moth - er, and scarce a sign didst deign the for - sak - en

du: von der Hei - math schei - dend kalt und
ones: From thy home thou stol - est cold and

stumm, bleich und schwei - gend
dumb! Pale and si - lent

auf der Fahrt, oh - ne
all the way, ate'st thou

Nah - rung, oh - ne Schlaf,
no - thing, sleep - less, too,

Belebend.
Animando.

starr und e - lend,   wild ver -
sick and trou - bled,   wild,   dis -

stört:_   wie er - trug' ich, so dich
traught: Could I bear it, thus to

Mässiger.
Più moderato.

se - hend,   nichts dir mehr zu sein,
see thee?   No - thing I to thee,

fremd vor dir zu steh'n?   O,   nun mel - de,
cold and strange to me?   Tell, oh tell me

was dich müht!   Sa - ge, kün - de,   was dich quält!
all thy care!   Tell me tru - ly   all thy fear!

B. Her-rin I - sol - de, trau - te-ste Hol - de, soll sie
La - dy, I love thee, none is a - bove thee! Oh! if

ff   *dim.*   *dim.*

Heftig belebend.
Animando con impeto.

B. werth sich dir wähnen, ver - trau - e nun Bran - gä - nen!
good she's to do thee, Bran - gæ-na now take to thee!

p   *dolce*   *p*   *sf*   *sf*   *p*

Isolda.

I. Luft! Luft! Mir er-stickt das Herz! Öff - ne!
Air! air! or my heart will burst! O - pen!

cresc.

I. Öff - - ne dort weit!
o - - pen there wide!

(Brangæna hastily draws apart the cur-

ff   *dim.*

tains in the centre)

p

Scene II.

One now looks down the whole length of the ship to the helm, and over the stern across the sea to the horizon. In the centre, about the main-mast, are sailors, busied with ropes, and lying about; beyond them, in the stern, are knights and attendants similarly disposed; somewhat apart stands Tristan, his arms folded, gazing thoughtfully out over the sea; at his feet lounges Kurvenal. From the mast-head above, the voice of the young sailor is heard again.

Mässig langsam. Andante moderato.

The young Sailor (at the mast-head, invisible)

Frisch weht der Wind der Hei-math zu:_ mein
The west-wind wild blows home-ward now:_ mine

i-risch Kind, wo wei-lest du? Sind's dei-ner Seuf-zer We-hen,
I-rish child, where lin-g'rest thou? Or is it, thou art try-ing

die mir die Se-gel blä-hen? We-he, we-he, du Wind!
to fill the sails, by sigh-ing? Blow then, wind fresh and wild!

Isolda (whose eyes have at once sought Tristan and fixed stonily on him_ aside, gloomily)

Mir er-ko-ren,_ mir ver-lo-ren,_
I mis-tak-en! I for-sak-en!_

Weh, ach we-he, mein Kind!
Woe, ah woe is my child!

18325

hehr und heil,___ kühn und feig!___ Tod - geweihtes
Bright and brave!___ Knight and knave!___ Death - de - vot - ed

Haupt!___ Tod - ge - weihtes Herz!___ Was hältst du von dem
head!___ Death - de - vot - ed heart!___ What think'st thou of the

(laughing unnaturally)

Knechte? Dort den Hel - den, der mei - nem Blick den sei - nen
var - let? There, the he - ro, who turns his eyes a - way from

Brangæna (following her eyes)

Wen meinst du?
Whom mean'st thou?

birgt, in Scham und Scheu - e ab - wärts schaut.___ Sag', wie
mine in fur - tive shame, and looks a - way:___ Speak, how

Brangæna.

dünkt er dich? Frägst du nach Tristan, theu-re Frau? dem Wun-der al - ler
like you him? Speak'st thou of Tristan, la - dy dear? That mar-vel of all

p cresc. *mf*

Rei-che, dem hoch - ge-pries'nen Mann, dem Helden oh-ne Gleiche, des
peoples, that man of high re-nown, that he-ro without e-qual,whose

sf *p* *sf*

Isolda (ironically).

Der za-gend vor dem Strei-che sich flüch-tet wo er
Who, shrinking from my whip-lash, wher - e'er he can, would

Ruh - mes Hort und Bann?
fame so wide has grown?

p *sfp* *p*

kann, weil ei - ne Braut er als Lei - che für sei - nen Herrn ge-
hide, while to his mas-ter he bring - eth a corpse to be his

cresc. *f* *sf*

I.

wann!   Dünkt es dich   dun-kel, mein Gedicht? Frag'ihn denn
bride!___   Think'st thou,there's   naught in what I say? He is a

ff dim.   *p*

I.

selbst,den frei-en Mann, ob mir zu   nah'n er wagt? Der   Eh - ren Gruss und zücht'ge
man, go ask him,then, if come to   me he dare? This   cai - tiff lord doth e'en neg-

f   *p*   *f*

(etwas gedehnt)
(poco steso)

I.

Acht vergisst der Her - rin der za - ge   Held,   dass ihr Blick ihn nur nicht er -
lect to greet his la - dy with due re - spect;   For he wants not her eye to

cresc.

I.

rei - che, den Hel - den oh - ne Glei - che!___ O,___ er weiss wohl, wär-
catch him, this knight with none to match him!   Oh,___ he knows why it

ff   *p*   *più p*   *pp*

I.

um!___ Zu dem Stol-zen geh', meld'ihm der Her-rin Wort! Meinem Dienst be-
is!___ Now to this Sir Pride bear you his la - dy's will! As my vas-sal

p

Brangæna.

reit, schleu-nig soll er mir nah'n. Soll ich ihn bit-ten, dich zu
bound straight-way let him come nigh. Shall I en-treat him to ap-

fp

Isolda.

grüssen? Be - feh-len liess' dem Eigenhol-de Furcht der Herrin ich, I -
proach thee? Nay, let my lord forth-with be told, he mind his mistress, me, I -

f   *f*   *p*

(At a gesture of command from Isolda, Brangæna leaves her, and hesitatingly
makes her way along the deck, past the busy sailors, to the stern; Isolda gazes
after her with a blank expression, and throws herself back on the couch, and so
remains, during what follows, her eyes steady fixed astern)

Gemächlich.
Comodo.

sol - de!
sol - da!

doch kräftig
ma energico

p   *p*

(Kurvenal sees Brangæna coming and, without rising, twitch-
es Tristan's cloak)

poco cresc.

18325

Kurvenal.

Hab'Acht Tri - - stan!
Beware, Tris - - tan!

Tristan (starting)

Bot - schaft von I - sol - de. Was ist?— I - sol - de?—
Sum - mons from I - sol - da! What's that?— I - sol - da?—

(He quickly masters himself as Brangæna
approaches and curtsies)

Mässig langsam.
Andante moderato.

rallent.

Von mei - ner Her - rin?— Ihr ge -
Art from my la - dy?— Doth her

horsam was zu hö - ren mel - det hö - fisch mir die trau - te Magd?
faithful hand-maid bring me aught for my o - bedience to o - bey?

Brangæna.

Mein Her - re Tri - stan, euch zu se - hen
My lord, Sir Tris - tan, Sir, your la - dy

18325

B. wünscht I - sol - de, mei-ne Frau.
bids you straight-way come to her.

T. Tristan.
Grämt sie die lan-ge Fahrt, die geht zu
Thinks she the journey long? 'Twill soon be

T. End; eh' noch die Son-ne sinkt, sind wir am Land.
o'er: Hap-ly ere e-ven-song we'll be a-shore.

B. Brangæna.
So mög' Herr
May't please Sir

T. Was mei-ne Frau mir be-feh-le, treulich sei's er-füllt.
What so my la-dy com-mands me, light-ly shall be done.

B. Tristan zu ihr geh'n: das ist der Her-rin Will!
Tris-tan go to her: that is my la-dy's will.

T. Wo dort die grü-nen
Where yon-der grass-y

18325

22

T. Flu-ren dem Blick noch blau sich fär-ben, harrt mein Kö-nig
mead-ows from dis-tance still are a-zure, for my la-dy

T. mei-ner Frau: zu ihm sie zu ge-lei-ten, bald nah'ich mich der Lichten;
waits my King: and soon to lead her to him, will I at-tend her Highness;

Brangæna.

B. Mein Her-re Tristan, hö-re wohl: dei-ne
My lord, Sir Tristan, hear, I pray: in her

T. Keinem gönnt' ich die-se Gunst.
I this guer-don grant to none.

B. Dienste will die Frau, dass du zur Stell' ihr nah-test, dort, wo sie dei-ner harrt.
service, she demands that you forthwith approach her, there where she waits for thee.

T. Auf je-der
In ev-'ry

18325

T.
Stel - le, wo ich steh', ge - treu - - lich dien' ich ihr, der
du - ty that I do, I tru - - ly serve her well, the

T.
Frau - en höch-ster Ehr'. Liess ich das Steu - er jetzt zur
crown of wo - man-kind. If I should straight-way leave the

T.
Stund', wie lenkt' ich si - cher den Kiel zu Kö - nig Mar-ke's
helm, how could I pi - lot her bark in safe - ty to King

Brangæna.

T. B.
Land? Tri - stan, mein Her - re, was höhnst ___ du mich?
Mark? Tris - tan, your lord - ship: why mock'st ___ thou me?

B.
Dünkt dich nicht deutlich die thör'ge Magd, hör' meiner Her - rin Wort!
Tak'st thou not clearly this fool-ish maid: Hear thou my la - dy's words!

18325

24

B.

So, hiess sie, sollt' ich sa - gen:— Be -
Thus, said she, should I tell thee, "Nay,

Gedehnt.
Steso.

B.

feh - len liess' dem Ei - genhol - de Furcht der Her-rin sie, I -
let my lord forth-with be told, he mind his mistress, me, I -

Lebhaft, doch nicht zu schnell.
Vivace, ma non troppo presto.

Tristan (quietly)

B.T.

sol - de. Was wohl er - wi - der-test du?
sol - da!" What an-swer think'st thou to make?

Kurvenal (springing up)

K.

Darf ich die Antwort sa - gen?
May I sup-ply the an-swer?

Kurvenal.

K.

Das sa - ge sie der Frau I - sold? Wer Kornwalls Kron' und
This shall she say to Dame I - sold? If England's fee and

18325

Eng - lands Erb' an Ir - lands Maid vermacht, der kann der Magd nicht
Corn - wall's crown to Ireland's maid are due, she can - not be the

ei - gen sein, die selbst dem Ohm er schenkt. Ein Herr der Welt,
giv - er's own, and be his un - cle's, too. A Man of Fate,

Tri - stan der Held! Ich ruf's: du sag's, und groll - ten mir tau - send Frau I - sol -
Tris - tan the Great! I've said: an there should scold us a thousand Dame I - sol -

(While Tristan by gestures tries to silence him, and Brangæna, offended, turns to
go away, Kurvenal, as she moves slowly away, sings after her at the top of his
voice)

Schneller.
Più mosso.

den. „Herr Morold zog zu Mee - re her, in
das. "To lay a tax on Cornish backs Sir

26

K.

Kornwall Zins zu ha - ben; ein Eiland schwimmt auf ö - dem Meer, da liegt er nun be-
Mo - rold once was fer - ried; 'mid tussocks damp, in dis - mal swamp, his bod - y now lies

cresc. *f* *p*

K.

gra - - ben! Sein Haupt doch hängt im I - ren - land, als
bur - - ied! His head, tho', went to I - rish lands, as

sf *p*

K.

Zins gezahlt von En - ge - land. Hei! unser Held Tri - stan, wie der Zins zah - len
tax - es sent by English hands. Here's to my lord Tris - tan! For a tax, he's the

cresc. *ff*

(Kurvenal, driven away by Tristan, goes below to the cabin; Brangæna, much disturbed,
comes back to Isolda, and closes the curtains behind her while the whole crew is heard
singing without)

K.

kann!"   *poco più mosso*
man!"   *Noch etwas beschleunigend*
Tenor.   *Ancora più mosso*

f

All the Men.   „Sein Haupt doch hängt im I - ren - land, als Zins gezahlt von
His head, tho', went to I - rish lands, as tax - es sent by

Bass.

f

f *p* *cresc.* *f* *p cresc.*

18325

En-ge-land.
Englishhands.

Hei! unser Held Tristan, wie der Zins
Here's to my lord Tristan! For a tax,

zah - len
he's the

Sehr lebhaft.
Allegro molto.

Scene III.

kann!"
man!"

(Isolda and Brangæna alone; the curtains are again completely closed)
(Isolda rises with a despairing gesture of wrath. Brangæna falls at her feet)

Brangæna.

Weh!   ach we-he! dies zu
Woe   is me that I must

dul - den!
bear   it!

Isolda (restraining herself from a furious outbreak)

più f

Brangæna.

ff *dim.* *p trem.*

Doch nun von Tristan! Ge-nau will ich's ver-nehmen. Ach, fra-ge nicht!
What now of Tristan? Tell all! for I must hear it! Oh, ask me not!

Isolda. **Brangæna.**

Frei sag's oh-ne Furcht! Mit höf'- schen Wor - ten wich er
Come, speak without fear! With court - ly phrase he par-ried

p *p* *p*

Doch als du deut - lich mahntest?
But when you told him clear-ly?

aus. Da ich zur Stell' ihn zu dir rief:
all. When I had bid him come forth-with:

cresc. *mf*

wo er auch steh', so sagte er, getreu - lich dien' er ihr, der Frauen höchster
What-e'er he did, said he to me, he tru - ly served thee well, the crown of wo-man-

sf *sf* *dim.* *p* *dolce* *tr*

Ehr'; liess' er das Steu-er jetzt zur Stund', wie lenkt' er si-chern den
kind. If he should straight-way leave the helm, how could he pi-lot the

cresc. *sf* *sf* *dim.* *p*

Etwas zurückhaltend.
Poco ritenuto.

Isolda (bitterly)
(sehr gedehnt)
(molto steso)

Kiel zu Kö-nig Mar-ke's Land? „Wie lenkt' er si-cher den
bark in safe-ty to King Mark? "How could he pi-lot the

p

Wieder sehr lebhaft.
Molto vivace, come prima.

Kiel zu Kö-nig Marke's Land!" — Den
bark in safe-ty to King Mark!" To

più p *p* *cresc.*

(grell und heftig)
(shrill and vehemently)

Zins ihm aus-zu-zah-len, den er aus Ir - land
pay the tax-es o - ver that he from Ire - land

f *f* *più f*

Brangæna.

zog! Auf dei-ne eig'- nen
brings! Thy message I de-

ff *mf*

18325

B.

Worte, als ich ihm die ent - bot, liess sei - nen Die - ner Kur - we - nal _
liv-er'd, aye, in thy ver - y words. Then said his ser - vant Kur - ve - nal _

Isolda.

I.

Den hab' ich wohl ver - nommen, kein Wort, das mir ent - ging. Er _
Ah! but I heard him al - so, no word of it was lost. And

sfp *p < sf* *p < sf*

I.

fuh - rest du mei - ne Schmach, _____ nun
now thou know - est my shame, _____ now

p < sf *p < cresc.* *sf* *più f*

I.

hö - - - - - re, was sie mir
hear _____ what brought it on

ff *f*

Sehr bewegt und wechselvoll im Zeitmass.
Con molto moto, vacillando il tempo.

I.

schuf. _ Wie lachend sie mir Lie - der
me. They smile and sing their songs a-

f *dim.*

I. sin- gen, wohl ____ könnt' auch ich er - wi - dern!
gainst me! Ah! ____ but I too could an - swer!

Mässiger.
Più moderato.

poco rall.
dim.

I. Von ei - nem Kahn, der klein und arm an
A - bout the skiff, so small, so poor, that

I. Irlands Kü - sten schwamm, da - rinnen krank ein sie - cher Mann e - lend ____
came to Ire - land's shore! And in it lay a wounded man, help - less ____

I. ____ im Ster - ben lag. I - sol - de's Kunst ward ihm be -
____ and dy - ing there. I - sol - da's skill he learned to

più p

I. kannt, mit Heil - sal - ben und Bal - sam - saft der
know; with salves sooth - ing, and heal - ing balms, the

rit.   *a tempo*

Wun - de, die ihn plag - te, ge-treu-lich pflag sie da. Der
wounds that so dis - tressed___ him she tend-ed faith-ful - ly. As

rit.   *a tempo*

più p   *dim.*   *pp*

Immer belebter.
Sempre più animato.

„Tan - tris" mit sor-gen-der List sich nann-te,   als
"Tan - tris" he cun-ning-ly had dis - guised him!   As

p   *cresc.*

Schneller.
Più mosso.

„Tri - stan" I - sold' ihn bald er - kann - te, da in des
"Tris - tan" I - sold' soon rec - og - nized him: His swordwhen

fp   *fp*   *fp*   *p*

Müss'- gen Schwer - te ei - ne Scharte sie ge-wahr - te, da-rin ge-
turn - ing o - ver, there a nick she did dis - cov - er, where fit-ted

nau sich fügt' ein Split - ter, den einst im Haupt des I - ren-
fair and square a sliv - er that in the head of Ire - land's

p   *cresc.-*

I.
rit - ter, zum Hohn ihr heim - ge - sandt, mit kund'- ger Hand sie
he - ro, sent home her pride to wound, her cun - ning hand had
f
Schnell.
Vivace.
fand. Da schrie's mir
found! Then cried a
ff
auf aus tief - stem Grund!
voice as from the grave:
dim.
ff
Mit dem hel - len Schwert ich vor ihm stund,
O'er him there I stood with that bright glaive,
f
an ihm, dem Ü - ber - fre - chen, Herrn Mo - rold's
to venge, on this ma - raud - er, Sir Mo - rold's
dim.
cresc.
ff

poco rallent.   *ritenuto*   **Sehr mässig.**
Molto moderato.

I.

Tod   zu   rä-chen.   Von sei-nem
shame - ful   mur-der.   Then from his

p   *dolce*
weich

I.

La-ger   blickt' er her,   nicht auf das
pal-let   looked he up,   not on the

p   *p*

Sehr zurückhaltend.
Molto ritardando.

I.

Schwert,   nicht auf die Hand,   er sah
sword,   nor on my hand   But deep

p molto cresc.   *ff*

I.

mir in die Au - gen.   Seines E - len-des jam-mer-te
in th'eyes he looked me,   and his help - less-ness trou-bled me

f

sehr ausdrucksvoll u. zart
molto espressivo e dolce

p

Langsam.
Lento.

p

I.

mich;   das Schwert   ich liess es fal - len!
sore;   the sword,   I   let fall from me!

cresc.   *sf*   *p*

Mässig.
Moderato.

I.

Die Mo-rold schlug, die Wun - - de, sie
That Mo-rold wound I tend - - ed, in

I.

heilt' ich, dass er ge-sun - de, und heim nach Hau - se
hope that, when it was mend - ed, he would for home de-

Schneller.
Più mosso.

I.

keh - re, mit dem Blick mich nicht mehr beschwe-re!
sert me, where his glanc - es no more should hurt me!

piùp

p *più p*

f

Brangæna.

B.

O Wun - der! Wo hatt' ich die Au-gen? Der
As-tound-ing! How blind have I been, then? The

dim.

p

Immer noch beschleunigend.
Ancora più mosso.

Isolda.

B.
I.

Gast, den einst ich pfle - gen half? Sein Lob hör - test du
guest whom once I helped to tend? But now thou heard'st his

cresc.

I. e - ben: „Hei! un-ser Held Tri - stan!“
prais - es: "Here's to my lord Tris - tan!"

I. Der war je - ner traur' - ge
He was that poor, wretch - ed

Sehr feurig.
Con molto fuoco.

I. Mann. Er
man. A

molto cresc.

ff

I. schwur mit tau - send Ei - den mir ew' - gen
thou - - sand oaths he swore me, how grate - ful

meno f

I. Dank und Treu - e!
he, how faith - ful!

dim. p

cresc. - - - - -

I.
Nun hör; wie ein Held Ei - de
Now hear, how a knight keeps his
ff
f
hält!
oath!
ff
dim.
Den als Tan - tris un - er-kannt ich ent-
For as Tan - tris, un - re-vealed, I re-
p
las-sen, als Tri-stan kehrt er kühn zu-rück;
leased him, as Tri-stan comes he brave-ly back;
fp
f
auf stol-zem Schiff, von ho-hem Bord, Ir-lands
and from his ship, so proud and high, Ire-land's
p
f
p
cresc.

Etwas gedehnt.
Poco steso.

Er - bin begehrt' er zur Eh' für Kornwalls mü-den Kö-nig, für
heir - ess he asks as a bride, for Corn-wall's ser-vile rul-er, his

ff *dim.*

rallent. **Schnell.**
Vivo.

Mar-ke, sei-nen Ohm. Da Mo - - rold
an-cient un-cle Mark. Were Mo - - rold

p *p cresc.* *f*

leb - te, wer hätt' es ge-wagt, uns
liv - ing, who ev - er had dared to

p *f* *f*
p *p*

je sol - che Schmach zu bie - ten? Für der zins - - pflicht'-gen
put such a slight up-on us, as that pay - - er of

p *f* *p*

Kor - nen-Für - sten um Ir - lands Kro - ne zu wer-ben!
Corn - ish trib - ute for Ire - land's crown should be suit-or!

cresc. *sf* *ff*

18325

poco rallent.

Ach, we - - he mir! Ich ja
Ah, woe - is me! I it

Mässig.
Moderato.

war's, die heim - lich selbst die Schmach sich
was that cov - ert - ly my shame be -

Belebt.
Animato.

schuf! Das rä - chen - de Schwert, statt es zu schwingen,
got! That sword of re - venge, wav -'ring un - wield - ed,

molto riten.

Noch mehr zurückhaltend.
Ancora più riten.

molto riten.

macht - los liess ich's fal - len! Nun
weak - ly fell be - fore me! Now

Wieder schnell.
Vivo, come prima.

dien' ich dem Va - sal - len!
rules my vas - sal o'er me!

18325

Brangæna.

Da Frie - de, Sühn' und Freund - -
When peace-ful truce and friend - -

schaft von Al - - - len ward be -
ship were sworn by both the

meno f

f *p* *molto cresc.* *f* *dim.*

schwo - ren, wir freu - ten uns All' des Tag's; wie ahn-te mir da, dass
peo - ples, how joy - ful we were that day! How could I fore-see the

p

dir es Kum - mer schüf'?
pain'twould bring to thee?

acceler.

p *f* *p* *f* *p* *molto cresc.* -

Isolda.

O blin - - de Au - gen! Blö - - de
Oh! eyes, how blind - ed! Heart, how

f *p* *f*

3 *3* *3* *3* *3* *3*

I.
Her - zen! Zah - mer Muth, ver - zag - tes
tim - id! Cour - age weak! A fu - tile
Schwei-gen! Wie an-ders prahlte Tri-stan aus, was ich verschlos-sen
si - lence! How brave-ly pour'd this Tris-tan forth, what I had nev - er
dim.
p
più p
Mässiger.
Meno mosso.
hielt! Die schwei - gend ihm das Le - ben
breathed! She who by si - lence gave him
pp
gab, vor Fein - des Ra - che ihn schwei - gend barg; was
life, from foes by si - lence she kept him safe; the
(steigernd)
(più appassionato)
acceler.
stumm ihr Schutz zum Heil ihm schuf,
si - lent care that wrought his weal
sfp cresc.

18325

Schnell.
Allegro.

mit ihr gab er es preis!
to her he dared re - veal!

Wie sieg - - prangend, heil und hehr,
How mas - - ter-ful, brave and bold,

laut und hell wies er auf mich:
turned he all eyes up-on me!

Etwas mässiger.
Poco più moderato.

„Das wär'
"A trea -

ein Schatz, mein Herr und Ohm; wie
- sure she, my liege and coz; what

dim.

cresc.

f

fp fp fp

dolce

più p

Noch mässiger.
Ancora più moderato.
dünkt euch die zur Eh? Die schmucke Irin hol' ich
think'st of her for bride? This Irish jewel will I
p dolce
Belebend.
Animando.
her; mit Steg und Wegen wohl bekannt, ein
bring; for ev'ry stock and stone know I; a
cresc.
Immer belebter.
Sempre più animato.
Wink, ich flieg' nach Irenland; Isolde, die ist
nod, and I'll to Ireland fly; Isolda is your
euer! mir
own, Sire! I
acceler.
più f
poco riten.
Sehr schnell.
Allegro molto.
lacht das Abenteuer!"
would I might be gone, Sire!"
poco riten.
ff
f

44

Fluch ___ dir, ___ Ver - ruch - ter!
Curse ___ thee, ___ thou das - tard!

Fluch ___
Curs'd ___

___ dei - nem Haupt!
___ be thy head!

Ra - che!
Ven - geance!

Tod! ___
Death! ___

Tod ___ uns Bei - den!
Death ___ for both, too!

Brangæna (flinging herself upon Isolda with unrestrained affection)

O Sü - sse!
O sweet-est!

Trau - te!
Mis - tress!

Theu - re!
Dear- est,

18325

B.
Hol - de! Gold' - ne
pur - est! Gold - en
ff
(She draws Isolda
Her - rin! Lieb' I - sol - de!
La - dy! Trust - ed sur - est!
toward the couch)
Hör' mich! Kom - me!
Hear me! Come, then!
decresc. poco a poco
Setz' dich her!
Sit thee here!
p
Immer noch sehr bewegt.
Sempre con molto moto.
Wel - cher Wahn! Welch' eit - les
This is false and base - less
mf

B. Zür - nen! Wie magst du dich be - thö - ren, nicht hell zu seh'n noch hö - ren?
an - ger! Thou look'st at all in - sane - ly, nor see'st or hear'st it plain - ly.

B. Was je Herr Tri - stan dir ver - dank - te, sag' konnt'er's hö - her
How - ev - er much Sir Tris - tan owes thee, how could he more re -

B. loh - nen, als mit der herr - lich - sten der Kro - nen? So dient' er
nown thee, than that as queen he now should crown thee? Thus serves he

B. treu ___ dem ed - len Ohm; dir
well ___ his no - ble king; he

B. gab er der Welt be - gehr - lich - sten Lohn: dem eig' - nen Er - be,
gives thee the world's most cov - et - ed prize! For all his for - tune,

Vocal line text:

echt und e - del, ent - sagt' er zu dei - nen Fü -
true and no - ble, be - fore thee he now dis - own -

ssen, als Kö - ni - gin dich zu
eth, when thee as a queen he

(Isolda turns away)

grü - ssen!
crown - eth!

Und warb er Mar - ke dir zum Ge - mahl, wie woll-test
And if to Mark he mar - ries thee now, why hast thou

du die Wahl doch schel - ten, muss er nicht werth dir gel - ten?
thus his choice re - sent - ed? Shouldst not be well con - tent - ed?

ausdrucksvoll
espressivo

B.

Von ed- -ler Art____ und mil-dem Muth, wer
Of no- -ble race____ and gen-tle ways, who

p sempre legato

B.

gli- -che dem Mann____ an Macht und Glanz?
e- -quals this man____ in might or fame?

cresc.

p

B.

Dem ein hehr- ster Held so treu-lich dient,
If a knight so no-ble serves him well,

p

p

B.

wer möch- te sein Glück nicht thei- -
shouldst thou, then, not be de- light-

cresc. - *- -*

p

B.

len, als Gat- -tin
ed, with him____ to

p

cresc. - *-*

Isolda (staring vacantly)

bei ihm wei – – – -len?
be u – nit – – -ed?

Un – – – – -ge -minnt___ den hehr – – -sten
Un – – – -be – loved,___ yet ev – – -er

Mann___ stets___ mir nah' zu se –
thus___ near to him so no – –

hen!___ wie könnt' ich die Qual be – ste-hen?
ble!___ How can I en – dure my trouble?

Brangæna.

Was meinst du Ar – ge? Un – – -ge -minnt?
How dar'st how say it? Un – – -be - loved?

$(\text{d.}=\text{d})$

p dolce

18325

(She comes toward Isolda coaxingly and caressingly)
B.
Wo
Where
p
ausdrucksvoll
espressivo
leb- -te der Mann, der dich nicht lieb-te? der I-sol-
lives there a man that would not love thee? He that sees
p
-den säh', und in I-sol-den se-
I-sol-da, would he not too glad-
p
sehr weich
dolcissimo
lig nicht ganz ver-ging'? Doch.
ly in love ex-pire? And
p
mf
der dir er-ko-ren, wär' er so kalt,
he that thou choos-est, waxed he e'er cold,
dim.
p
mf

zög' ihn von dir ein Zau-ber ab, den
drew him some spell from thee a-way, I'd

Bö-sen wüsst' ich bald zu bin-
quick-ly find some way to hold

-den; ihn bann-te der Min-ne
him, and bind him in ma-gic

(Coming close to Isolda with a mien of mysterious familiarity)

Macht.
love.

Kennst du der
Know'st thou not

Mut-ter Kün-ste nicht?
well thy mother's skill?

Wähnst du, die Al-les klug er-
Think'st thou that she, that all fore-

B.
wägt, oh - ne Rath in frem-des Land hätt' sie mit dir mich ent-
sees, un-pre - pared had bid-den me to seek far coun - tries with

Etwas langsamer.
Poco più lento.

Isolda (darkly)

B.
I.
sandt? Der Mut - ter Rath gemahnt mich
thee? My mother's arts I know full

I.
recht; willkom - men preis' ich ih - re Kunst:
well, and glad - ly now I welcome them:

I.
Ra - che für den Ver - rath,— Ruh' in der Noth dem
Ven-geance for trea-son they,— rest when the heart is

Brangæna.

I.
B.
Herzen!— Den Schreindort bring' mir her! Er birgt, was heil dir
troubled! That cas - ket fetch me here! Here lies a cure for

Etwas belebend.
Poco animando.

fromnt.___
thee.
(She fetches a small gold box, opens it, and indicates its contents)

p
poco cresc.

So   reih-te sie die   Mut-ter,   die   mächt'gen Zau-
Thy   moth-er thus ar-ranged them,   these   might-y, ma-

p dolce

-bertränke:
-gic potions:
Für Weh' und Wun-den Bal-sam hier,
For pain and wounds a balm is   here,

p
p

(She takes out a small vial)

für bö-se Gif-te Ge-   gen-gift.___
for e-vil poi-son, an-   ti-dotes.___

molto rallent.

p dolce

18325

a tempo **Mässig.**
Moderato,

B.
Den hehr-sten Trank,__ ich halt'__ ihn
The great-est draught, I have__ it

a tempo

f **p** *dolce*

Isolda.

B.
I.
hier.__   Du irrst,__ ich kenn'__ ihn
here.__   You're wrong__ I know it

più **p**   **pp**

I.
bes-ser;   ein star-kes Zei - chen schnitt ich ihm
bet-ter.   I deep-ly drew a mark on the

pp   **p**

I.
ein.__   (She seizes a vial and shows it)
one.__

cresc. poco a poco

I.
Der Trank ist's, der mir
This draught will do me

ff   **p**

2/2

18325

Schnell.
Presto.

(She has risen from the couch and listens with rising dread to the cries of the seamen)

I.

taugt!
good!

Brangæna.

(She recoils in horror)

Der To- -des-trank!
That death - ly draught!

Tenor I.

Ho! he! ha! he! ho! he! ha! he!___
Yo heave o! heave o! heave o! heave___

Seamen (without) **Bass I.**

Am Un-termast die Se - gel ein!
Stand by the sheet! Haul down the sail!

Isolda.

Das deu- -tet schnel - le
How quick- -ly we have

Tenor I.

_ ho!___ he! ___ ho!___
_ o!___ heave___ o!___

Tenor II.

Am Un - ter-mast die Se - gel ein!
Stand by the sheet! Haul down the sail!

Bass I II.

Ho! he! ha! he! ho! he! ha! he!
Yo heave o! heave o! heave o! hey!

18325

I.

Fahrt!
come!

Weh mir! Na - he das
Woe's me! Here is the

(strepitoso)

Scene IV.

(Through the curtains enters Kurvenal unceremoniously)

Lebhaft.
Vivace. (♩.=♩)

I.
K.

Kurvenal.

Land!
land!

Auf!
Up!

Auf!
Up!

Ihr
ye

f

K.

Frau - - - - -en!
wo - - - - -men!

f

f

K.

Frisch und froh! Rasch ge-rü-stet! Fer-tig nun, hur-tig und flink!
Look a - live! Come, be mov-ing! Stead-y and read-y and spry!

dim. - - - -

p

cresc.

K. Und Frau I- -sol-den sollt' ich sa-gen von
For Dame I- -sol-da I've a message, from

K. Held Tri-stan, mei-nem Herrn: Vom Mast der Freu-de
Tris-tan, that is_ my lord: Our ban-ner from_ the

cresc. f p dolce

K. Flag-ge, sie we-he lu-stig ins Land; in
mast-head, is wav-ing gai-ly a-shore; King

un poco cresc.

K. Mar- -ke's Kö-nigsschlos- -se
Mark_ with-in_ his cas- -tle

più cresc.

K. mach' sie ihr Nah'n_ be-kannt.
thus knows of our_ ap-proach.

K. Drum Frau I - sol - de bät er ei - - len, fürs
Will Dame I - sold be pleased to hur- -ry, pre -

ff

K. Land sich zu be - rei - - -
pared to leave the wa - - -

ff   **ff**

K. ten, dass er sie könnt' ge - lei - -ten.
ter, that so he may es - cort her.

tr

p   *cresc.*   **f**   **ff**

Mässig.
Moderato. (♩=♩.)

Isolda (who was at first startled at the summons, now composedly and with dignity)

Herrn
Sir

ff

3   3   3

3   3

Tri-stan brin-ge mei-nen Gruss, und meld' ihm, was ich
Tris-tan may'st thou greet from me, and say how I have

sa-ge. Sollt' ich zur Seit' ihm ge-hen, vor Kö-nig Mar-ke zu
spo-ken: If I should walk be-side him, when to his monarch he

ste-hen, nicht möcht' es nach Zucht und Fug ge-scheh'n, em-
hied him, then would it be nei-ther meet nor right, un-

pfing' ich Süh-ne nicht zu-vor für un-ge-sühnte Schuld:
less I first had par-doned him for what of-fense he gave:

(Kurvenal makes a gesture of defiance)

drum such' er mei-ne Huld.
So let him par-don crave.

18325

(mit Steigerung)
(con impeto)

Du mer - ke wohl und meld' es gut!
Thou, mark me well, and bear it straight!

Nicht woll' ich mich be - rei - ten, ans Land ihn zu be -
She will not leave the wa - ter, nor he to land es -

(sich mässigend)
(moderando)

glei - ten; nicht werd' ich zur Seit' ihm ge - hen, vor
cort her, nor yet would she walk be - side him, when

Kö - nig Mar - ke zu ste - hen, be - gehrte Ver - ges - sen und Ver - ge - ben nach
to King Mark he hied him, un - less to for-give him and for-get, he shall

Zucht und Fug er nicht zu - vor für un - ge - büss - te Schuld:
ask me first, as he should do. For what of-fense he gave,

Kurvenal.

die böt' ihm mei-ne Huld!
my par-don he may have.

Si-cher wisst, das
Wit you well, I'll

sag' ich ihm; nun harrt, wie er mich hört!
tell him this; now wait, how he will hear!

Sehr bewegt.
Molto mosso.

p molto cresc.

(Isolda hurries to Brangæna and embraces her warmly)

Isolda.

Nun leb'
Fare thee

wohl, Bran-gä- -ne! Grüss' mir die
well, Bran-gæ- -na! Fare- -well to

ff

f

p

poco riten.

Welt, grü- -sse mir Va- -ter und
earth! Greet me my fa- -ther and

f

dim.

p

p

Schnell.
Presto. Brangæna.

Mut-ter! Was ist? Was sinnst du? Woll-test du flieh'n? Wo-hin soll ich dir
mother! What say'st? What mind'st thou? Think'st thou to fly? Where then am I to

Mässig und zurückhaltend.
Moderato e ritenuto.

(Isolda swiftly regains self-control)

fol - gen?
fol - low?

f dim.   *più p*

Isolda.

Hör - test du nicht? Hier bleib' ich, Tri - stan will ich er -
Hast thou not heard? Here stay I; Tris - tan will I a -

pp   *p*   *p*

war - ten.___ Ge - treu be-folg'was ich be - fehl': den
wait here.___ Now fol-low close what I com - mand: the

pp   *p*   *p*

(Isolda takes the vial
from the casket.)
Brangæna.

Süh - ne-trank rü - ste schnell;___ du weisst, den ich dir wies? Und
draught of truce, mix it quick:___ thou know'st, the one I show'd? Which

p   *p*   *p*

18325

Isolda.

wel-chen Trank? / Die - sen Trank! / In die gold'-ne Schale giess' ihn aus; ge-
was the one? / Here's the one! / In that gold-en goblet pour it out; 't will

cresc. — *ff* — *dim.* —

Schnell.
Presto.

füllt fasst sie ihn ganz.
al - most fill it full.

p f

Sei ___ du mir treu!
Canst ___ thou be true?

Brangæna (taking the vial in terror)

Trau' ich den Sinn? / Den Trank für
Can this be true? / For whom the

più f — *ff* — *dim.*

Wer mich be - trog. / Trin - ke mir
Him that be - trayed! / Truce will he

wen? / Tri- -stan?
draught? / Tris- -tan?

p — *f* — *dim.*

18325

64

Brangæna (throwing herself at Isolda's feet)

Süh - - ne!
pledge me!

Entset - zen!
O hor - ror!

p cresc. — — — — — — *ff* — *f*

Isolda (with great vehemence)

Scho - ne mich Ar - me!
Pit - y, I pray thee!

Scho - - ne du
Pit - - y thou

ff — *f* — *ff*

3 3 3 3

mich, un - treu - e Magd!
me, O faith-less maid!

più f

ff

3 3 3 3 3 3 3

Allmählich etwas zurückhaltend.
Poco a poco ritenuto.

Kennst du der Mut-ter Kün-ste nicht?
Know'st thou not well my mother's skill?

Wähnst du, die Al - les klug er-
Think'st thou that she, who all — fore-

dim.

wägt,
sees,

oh - ne Rath in fremdes Land hätt' sie mit dir mich ent-
un - pre-pared had bid-den me to seek far coun-tries with

p

dim.

For pain and wounds a salve she gave me,
Für Weh' und Wun-den gab sie Bal-sam,

sandt?
thee?

Gedehnt und langsam.
Lento e steso.

für bö - se Gif - te Ge - gen-gift: für
for e - vil poi - sons, an - ti - dotes: for

Wieder bewegter.
Più mosso come prima.

tief - stes Weh', für höch - stes Leid
deep - est woe, for keen - est pain,

gab sie den To - - des-trank. Der
gave she the draught of death. Let

Langsam. Lento.
Brangæna (almost beside herself)

Tod nun sag' ihr Dank! O tief - stes
Death, then, thank her now! O deep - est

18325

Isolda.
poco accel.
molto acceler.
I.
Gehorchst du mir nun?
Now wilt thou o - bey?
Bist du mir treu?
Canst thou be true?
B.
molto acceler.
Weh'!
woe!
O höch - stes Leid!
O keen - est pain!
Der Trank?
The draught?
Kurvenal (entering)
K.
Herr
Sir
poco accel.
molto acceler.
p
poco cresc.
molto cresc.
Lebhaft.
Vivace.
(Brangæna rises, terrified and confused. Isolda strives with a mighty effort to compose herself)
K.
Tri - stan!
Tris - tan!
f
f
più f
Etwas zurückhaltend.
Poco ritenuto.
ff
dim.
Isolda (to Kurvenal)
I.
Herr Tri - stan tre - te
Sir Tris - tan may draw
più p
p

Scene V.

(Kurvenal retires again. Brangæna, scarcely mistress of herself, turns towards the back. Isolda, summoning all her powers to meet the crisis, walks slowly and with effort to the couch, leaning on the head of which she then stands, her eyes fixed on the entrance.)

Langsam. Lento.

nah'!
nigh!

(Tristan enters and pauses respectfully at the entrance)

(Isolda, a prey to violent agitation, gazes on him intently)

68

Tristan.

Begehrt, Her - rin, was ihr wünscht.
Command, la - dy, what you wish.

Isolda.

Wüss-test du nicht, was ich be - geh-re, da doch die
Tho' un - a - ware what were my wishes, was it not

Furcht, mir's zu er - fül - len, fern mei-nem Blick dich hielt?
fear to un - der-take them, kept thee from out my sight?

Tristan. / **Isolda.**

Ehrfurcht hielt mich in Acht. Der Eh - re
Hon- our held me in awe. Small hon - our,

we - nig bo - test du mir; mit off'-nem Hohn ver-wehrtest du Ge-
tru - ly, gav - est thou me; with sheer con-tempt hast thou re-fused o-

18325

hor-sam mei-nem Ge- bot. Ge-hor-sam ein- zig
bedience un-to my call. O- bedience on- ly

Tristan.

Isolda.

So dankt' ich Ge- rin-ges dei-nem Herrn,
Small thanks has thy mas-ter, then, from me,

hielt mich in Bann.
kept me a- way.

rieth dir sein Dienst Un- sit-te ge-gen sein ei- gen Ge-mahl?
if serv-ing him makes you un-man-ner-ly toward his be-trothed!

Tristan.

Sit- te lehrt, wo ich ge- lebt: zur Braut- fahrt der
Cus- tom says, where I have lived: Ere mar- riage, the

Isolda.

Brautwer-ber mei- de fern die Braut. Aus wel-cher Sorg'?
bride-bring-er keeps him from the bride. And wherefore so?

18325

Tristan.
Fragt die Sit - te!
Ask the cus - tom!

Isolda.
Da du so

sitt - sam, mein Herr Tri - stan, auch ei - - ner
cus - tom, my lord Tris - tan, one oth - - er

gehalten tenuto *poco cresc.*

Sit - te sei nun ge - mahnt: den Feind dir zu
cus - tom let me re - call: from foe well to

süh - nen, soll er als Freund dich rüh - men. Und wel - chen
ward thee, let him as friend re - gard thee. And who's my

Tristan.

cresc.

Isolda.
Feind? Frag' dei - ne Furcht!
foe? Ques - tion thy fear!

molto cresc. *ff* *f*

Blut-schuld schwebt zwi-schen uns. Die ward gesühnt. Nicht zwischen
'Twixt us blood - guilt - i - ness! That was for-giv'n. Not be-tween

uns! Im off'-nen Feld, vor al - lem Volk ward
us! In o - pen field, 'fore all the folk, a

Etwas bewegter, doch mässig.
Poco più mosso, ma moderato.

Ur - feh - de ge - schwo-ren. Nicht da war's, wo ich
feud - truce has been sworn to. 'Twas not then that I

Tan - tris barg, wo Tri - stan mir ver - fiel. Da
Tan - tris hid and Tris - tan hos-tage held. Then

stand er herr - lich, hehr und heil;
stood he lord - ly, brave and bright;

18325

doch was er schwur, das schwur ich nicht:_ zu
yet what he swore, that swore not I:_ I

schwei - gen hatt' ich ge - lernt.
school'd my - self to be still.

Da in stil - ler
In my qui - et

Belebend.
Animando.

Kam - mer krank er lag,
cham - ber sick he lay,

mit dem Schwer-te stumm ich vor ihm stund:
with his sword I stood be - fore him, dumb:

schwieg da mein Mund,
No word I spoke,

Sehr lebhaft.
Molto vivace.

bannt' ich meine Hand; doch
lift- -ed not a hand. But

was einst mit Hand und Mund ich ge-lobt, das
all that with hand and voice I'd re-solv'd, I

schwur ich schweigend zu hal-ten. Nun
swore in si-lence to do, then. Now,

Wieder mässiger.
Più moderato.

Tristan.

will ich des Ei - des wal-ten. Was schwurt ihr,
now let my oath come true, then! What didst thou

acceler.   Isolda (quickly)   riten.
Tristan (quietly)

Frau? Ra - che für Mo-rold! Müht euch
swear? Ven - geance for Mo-rold! Car'st for

18325

74

Lebhafter.
Più vivo.

Isolda (animatedly)

T. I.

die? Wagst du zu höh - nen?_
that? Dar'st thou to scorn me?_

cresc.   ff   dim.

Ped.   *

I.

An - ge - lobt war er mir, der heh - re
I was plight - ed to him, the glo - rious

p   dolce

I.

I - ren - held; sei - ne Waf - fen hatt' ich ge -
I - rish lord, and his weap - ons all had I

p

I.

weiht; für mich zog er zum Streit.
blessed; for me went he to war,

cresc.-   f

Noch etwas mehr belebend.
Ancora più animando.

I.

Da er ge - fal - len, fiel mei - ne Ehr; in des Her - zens
and at his fall - ing, my hon-our fell. When my heart was

f   p   cresc. -

fp   fp

18325

Schwe - re schwur ich den Eid: würd' ein
break - ing, made I this vow: If no

Mann den Mord nicht süh - nen, wollt' ich
man his quest would make it, I, a

Etwas mässiger.
Poco più moderato.

Magd mich dess' er - küh - nen.
maid, would un - der - take it.

Siech und matt in mei - ner Macht,
Sick and weak and in my power,

Belebter. Più animato.

war - um ich dich da nicht schlug,
Where - fore I slew thee not there,

Mässiger.
Più moderato.
(zurückhaltend)
(ritenuto)

Belebend.
Animando.

das sag' dir selbst mit leich-tem Fug:_ Ich pflag des
is clear e-nough, as thou shalt hear:_ Thee watched I

Wun-den, dass den heil Ge-sun-den
o-ver, that thou might'st re-cov-er,

cresc.

rä-_-chend schlü-ge der Mann, der I-sol-den ihn ab-ge-
fierce-_-ly slaugh-ter'd to be, at I-sol-da's ex-press de-

Mässig.
Moderato.
(etwas gedehnt)
(poco steso)

wann._ Dein Los nun
cree!_ Thy fate thou

dim.   p

pp

f

sel-ber magst du dir sa-gen! Da die
now canst sure-ly fore-tell_ thee! If the

p

cresc.

I.

Män - ner sich all' ihm ver - tra - gen, wer muss nun Tri - stan
men are con - tent to o - bey_ thee, who is there left to

I.

schlagen?
slay thee?

rallent.

ff *dim.*

Langsam.
Lento. Tristan (pale and gloomy)

T.

War Mo-rold dir so werth, nun wie-der nimm das
If Mo-rold was so dear, take then this sword I

p *più p* *pp* *pp*

(He offers her his sword)

T.

Schwert, und führ' es si - cher und fest, dass du nicht dir's ent-fal - len
bear, and drive it fair - ly and straight, lest it fail thee, as once of

cresc. *p* *f* *p*

Etwas bewegter.
Poco più mosso. Isolda.

T.
I.

lässt! Wie
late! How

pp

18325

I.

sorgt' ich schlecht um dei- nen Her- ren; was wür- de Kö- nig Mar - ke
ill a turn I'd do thy mas- ter! How, think you now, King Mark would

I.

sa- gen, er- schlüg' ich ihm den be- sten Knecht, der Kron' und Land ihm ge-
take it, if I should slay his fore- most man, who won him king- dom and

I.

wann, den al- ler- treu'- sten Mann? Dünkt dich so
rights, the best of all his knights? Think'st thou so

I.

we- nig, was er dir dankt, bringst du die I - rin ihm_ als Braut, dass er nicht
small his thanks be to thee, thou that hast brought me as_ his bride, he'd not be

I.

schöl- te, schlüg' ich den Wer- ber, der Ur- feh- de- Pfand so treu ihm lie- fert zur
an- gerd, slew I the woo- er, who brings him so good a pledge of truce to the

Langsamer.
Più lento.

accel.

Hand? Wah - re dein Schwert! Da einst ich's schwang, als
feud? Sheathe thou the sword. I once did wield, when

mir ___ die Ra - che im Bu - sen rang,
thoughts ___ of ven-geance my bo - som filled,

als dein mes - sen-der Blick mein Bild sich stahl, ob ich Herrn
when thy crit - i - cal glance my like - ness took, if for his

Mar - ke taug' als Ge - mahl: das Schwert_
bride King Mark_ me would brook: The sword_

da liess ich's sin-ken.__ Nun lass uns Süh - ne
I let it fall then.__ So drink a truce to

18325

80

Mässig.
Moderato.
(She signs to Brangæna, who cowers and trembles as she moves)

trin - ken!
all, then!

(Isolda urges her with more emphatic gestures)
accel.

Mässig. (Brangæna sets about preparing the
Moderato. draught)

Voices of the Sailors (without)
Tenor I.

Ho! he! ha! he! ho! he! ha! he!
Yo! heave O! heave! Yo! heave O! heave

Bass I.

Am O - ber - mast die Se - gel ein!
Stand by the top! Haul down the sail!

18325

ha! — he! — ha! —
O! — heave O! —

Tenor II. *ff*
Am O-ber-mast ——— die Se - gel ein!
Stand by the top! ——— Haul down the sail!

Ho! he! ha! he!
Yo! heave O! hey!

Bass II. *ff*
Ho! he! ha! he! ho! he! ha! he!
Yo! heave O! heave O! heave O! hey!

Tristan (starting from his moody silence)   **Isolda.**

Wo sind wir? Hart am
Where are we? Right at

Ziel! Tri - stan, ge-winn' ich Süh - ne? Was
land! Tris - tan, is peace be - tween us? What

hast du mir zu sa - gen?
an - swer dost thou make me?

Tristan (darkly)

Des Schweigens Her-rin heisst mich schweigen:— fass' ich, was sie ver-
The queen of si-lence makes me si-lent:— Know-ing what she with-

schwieg, verschweig' ich, was sie nicht fasst.
held, with-hold I more than she knows.

accel. **Isolda** (with more animation)

Dein Schweigen fass' ich, weichst du mir
I know that si-lence_ thou wouldst re-

Lebhafter.
Più vivace.

aus. Wei - gerst du die Süh - ne mir?
fuse. Dost ___ thou then my truce de - cline?

Sailors (without)
Tenor I. II.

Ho! he! ha! he! ho! he! ha! he! ___ ha! ___
Yo! heave O! heave O! heave O! heave O!

Bass I. II.

Ho! he! ha! he!
Yo! heave O! hey!

Bass I. II.

(On an impatient sign from Isolda, Bran-

Ho!   he!   ha!   he!
Yo!   heave   O!   hey!

ff

gæna hands her the full goblet)   **Isolda** (advancing with the cup to Tristan, who gazes fixedly

ff   *ff*

Du hörst den Ruf?
Thou hear'st the call?

f

in her eyes).

Wir sind am Ziel: in kur- zer
We are at land: be- fore King

dimin.

rallent.   (very earnestly)   (with veiled scorn)

Frist steh'n wir vor Kö- nig
Mark we shall ere- long be

p *rallent.*   *pp*   *p*

Etwas gedehnt.
Poco steso.

Mar- ke.   Ge- lei- test du mich, dünkt dich's nicht
standing.   And leadst thou me then, were it not

p   *p*

I.
lieb, darfst du so ihm sa - gen:
well, if thou thus couldst greet him:
p
I.
„Mein Herr und Ohm, sieh' die dir
"My lord and king, look well on
poco cresc.
I.
an: ein sanf-t'res Weib gewannst du nie. Ih - ren
her: a ten-d'rer wife thou ne'er couldst win. Her be -
dimin.
p
I.
An - ge-lob - ten er - schlug ich ihr einst, sein Haupt sandt' ich ihr
troth - ed lov - er I slew, of a truth; his head I sent her
poco cresc.
mf

heim; die Wun - de, die sei - ne Wehr mir schuf, die
home; the wounds that his weap-ons wrought on me, she
p dolce
dolce
hat sie hold ge - heilt; mein Le - - - ben
gra - cious - ly did heal; my life with -
p
p poco cresc.
lag in ih - rer Macht: das schenk - te mir die
in her hand was laid: she gave it me, this
molto cresc.
f
ff
p
accel.
mil - de Magd, und ih - res Lan - des Schand' und
mer - ci - ful maid; and all her coun - try's slights and
accel.
p
molto cresc.
rall.
a tempo
Schmach, die gab sie mit dar - ein, dein Eh' - ge - mahl zu sein.
shame, she let them go, as well, with thee as queen to dwell.
f
rall.
p
a tempo
p

I.

So gu - ter Ga - ben hol - der Dank schuf mir ein sü - sser Süh - ne -
Such good-ly gifts I have to thank, with her a draught of truce I

I.

trank; den bot mir ih - re Huld, zu
drank; that par-don for me won, for

Sehr bewegt.
Molto animato.

I.

süh - nen al - le Schuld."
all the wrong I'd done."

Sailors (without)
Tenor.

Auf das Tau!
Ca - ble out!

Bass.

cresc.

An - ker los!
An - chor free!

Tristan (startling wildly)

Los den
Drop the

An - ker! Das Steu - er dem Strom!
an - chor! Her stern to the tide!

Den
And

Win - - - den Se - gel und Mast!
hold the sail to the wind!

(He snatches the cup from her)

Wohl kenn'ich Ir - lands Kö - ni - gin und ih - rer
Well known is Ire - land's queen to me, and all her

18325

88

Kün - ste Wun - der - kraft. Den Bal - sam
won - drous ma - gic might. The balm I

nützt' ich, den sie bot: den Be - cher nehm' ich nun, dass ganz
used, she bade me take; this bea - ker quaff I now, that right-

ich heut' ge - ne - se.
ly I re - cov - er.

Und ach - te auch des Süh - ne - eids, den ich zum Dank dir
Take heed, then, to my oath of truce, that thank - ful - ly I

sa - ge!
swear thee! *marcato*

18325

(gedehnt)
(allargando)

T. Tri - stan's Eh - re— höch - ste Treu'! Tri - stan's E - lend—
Tris - tan's honour— firm - est faith! Tris - tan's an - guish—

(Der Vortrag des Sängers zu beachten!)
(Colla parte.)

meno f *p* *cresc.* *f*

f *f* *ff*

(rasch) **(zögernd)** **(langsam)** **(gesteigert)**
(vivo) *p* **(ritenuto)** **(lento)** *più p* **(appassionato)**

T. kühn - ster Trotz! Trug des Herzens! Traum der Ah - nung! Ew' - ger
bold - est gage! Loss of courage! Dream of long - ing! End - less

sf *sf* *p* *più p* *p* *fp*

(etwas breit)
(poco allargando)

T. Trauer einz' - ger Trost: Ver - ges - sens güt' - ger Trank,
sor - row's on - ly salve: For - get - ful - ness I drink!

fp *ff* *p*

Sehr lebhaft.
Molto vivo.
(He puts the cup to his
lips and drinks) **Isolda.**

(lebhafter)
(animato)

T. dich trink' ich son - der Wank! Be - trug auch
I. All this, and do not shrink! Be - fooled e'en

p *f* *p* *f*

3 *3*

18325

90

(She wrests the cup from him)

hier? / here? Mein die Hälf-te! / Half for me, now!

Ver-rä-ther! / Be-tray-er!

(She drinks)

Ich trink' sie dir! / I drink to thee!

molt'espress. ff

Langsam. / Lento.

(Then she throws away the goblet.—They both shudder, and gaze into one another's eyes with the utmost emotion, but without changing their position, while their death-defiant expression changes to the glow of passion.)

sempre pp

18325

Trembling seizes them. They clutch their hearts tightly _____

Etwas bewegt.
Poco mosso.

and then pass their hands over
their brows. _____

Langsam.
Lento.

Again try to meet each other's
eyes _____

lower their eyes in confusion, then raise then again to each

other with increasing longing.)

Isolda (with trembling voice)

(sinking upon his breast)

Tri - stan!
Tris - tan!

Treu - lo - ser Hol - der!
Treach - er - ous dar - ling!

Tristan (with an outburst)

(He embraces her passionately)

I - sol - de!
I - sol - da!

cresc.

Lebhaft mit Steigerung.
Allegro appassionato.
Tristan.

(They remain in a silent embrace)

Se - lig - ste Frau!
Wom - an di - vine!

fp *cresc.*

All the Men (without)
Tenor I.

Tenor II.

Bass I.

Bass II.

ff

Heil! Kö - nig Mar - ke Heil!
Hail! to King Mark all hail!

sempre più f

(Brangæna, who with averted face was leaning bewildered and trembling over the side of the ship, now turns and sees the lovers clasped in each other's arms, and rushes forward, wringing her hands in despair)

Brangæna.

We — he! Weh'!
Woe — is me!

Mar - ke Heil!
Mark all hail!

Un - ab - wend - bar ew' - - ge Noth für kur - zen
End - less sor - row, not - - the breath of in - stant

Tod! Thör' - - ger Treu - - e
death! Fool - - ish, faith - - ful

trug - vol - les Werk blüht nun jam -
fraud's hand - i - work now breaks wail -

(Both start from their embrace)

- - mernd em - por!
- - ing a - broad!

ff ff p dolce

Tristan (confused)

Was träum - - te mir von
What dream was mine of

cresc.

Ped.

T. Tri - stan's Eh - - - re?
Tris - tan's hon - - - our?

ff *p dolce*

Isolda.

I. Was träum - te mir von I - sol - - de's
What dream was mine of I - sol - - da's

cresc. *Ped.* *Ped.*

I. Schmach?_____ Du mich ver-
shame?_____ I to re-

Tristan.

T. Du mir ver - lo - ren?
I, I to lose thee?

ff *p* *fp*

I. sto - ssen? Thö - ri - gen Zür - nens eit - les Dräu'n!
pel thee? Fol - ly and an - ger's i - dle threats!

T. Trü - genden Zau - bers tü - cki - sche List! I -
Ma - gic's mis - lead - ing, treach - er - ous tricks! I -

fp *fp* *cresc. -*

Tri - - - stan! Trau - te - ster
Tris - - - tan! Tru - - est of

sol - - - de! Sü - sse-ste Maid!
sol - - - da! Sweet - est of maids!

ff *ff*

Mann! Wie sich die Her - zen wo - gend er - he - ben, wie al - le
men! Ah! how our hearts are heav - ing and swell - ing! How ev - 'ry

Wie sich die Her - zen wo - gend er - he - ben, wie al - le
Ah! how our hearts are heav - ing and swell - ing! How ev - 'ry

p *f* *p* *f* *cresc.*

p *f* *p* *f* *cresc.*

p *f* *p* *f* *p cresc.*

Sin - ne won - nig er - be - - ben! Seh - nen - der
sense is throb - bing and thrill - - ing! Long - - ings of

Sin - ne won - nig er - be - - ben! Seh - nen - der
sense is throb - bing and thrill - - ing! Long - - ings of

p

p

f *p*

I.
Min - ne schwel - len-des Blü - - hen,
pas - sion, bud - ding and blow - - ing,
T.
Min - ne schwel - len-des Blü - - hen,
pas - sion, bud - ding and blow - - ing,
cresc.
I.
schmach - ten-der Lie - be se - li-ges Glü - hen!
year - nings with love's in - ten - si-ty glow - ing!
T.
schmach - ten-der Lie - be se - li-ges Glü - hen! Jach
year - nings with love's in - ten - si-ty glow - ing! Brings
f cresc.
I.
Jach in der Brust jauch - zen-de Lust! Tri -
Brings to each breast rap - ture and zest! Tris -
T.
in der Brust jauch - zen-de Lust! I - sol-de!
to each breast rap - ture and zest! I - sol-da!
più f
f

I. stan! Tri - - stan! Wel - -
tan! Tris - - tan! World, ___

T. I - sol - de! I - sol - - -
I - sol - da! I - sol - - -

più f ^ ^ *ff* *p*

I. - ten ___ ent - ron - nen, du ___ mir ge - won - - nen,
___ there ___ is none now, thee ___ have I ___ won ___ now,

T. - - - - de, I - sol - - - de mir ge -
- - - - da, I - sol - - - da, I have

I. Tri - stan! Du mir ___ ge - won - nen, du mir
Tris - tan! Thee have ___ I won - me, thee a -

T. won - nen! I - sol - - de! Du mir
won thee! I - sol - - da! Thee a -

p cresc.

I. ein — — — — — — — — zig bewusst, höch — — ste
lone — — — — — — — — I re-quire, thou — my

T. ein — — zig be-wusst, höch — — — ste
lone — — — I re-quire, thou — — my

piú f

I. Lie — — — — — — — — bes — de —
heart's — — — — — — — — _dimin._

T. Lie — — — — — — — — bes — de —
heart's — — — — — — — — _dimin._

f _dimin._ _p molto cresc._

(The curtains are thrown wide apart; the whole ship is crowded with knights and sailors who joy-
fully wave signals to the shore, which is now seen close at hand, crowned with a castle)

I. lust!
sire!
Brangæna. (to the women who, at a signal from her, come up from the cabin) (rushing between Tristan and Isolda)

B. Schnell, den Man-tel, den Kö-nigs-schmuck!
Quick, the man-tle, the roy-al robe!

(Tristan and Isolda remain lost in contemplation of each other, without noticing what is going on about them)

T. lust!
sire!

piú f

18325

Etwas zurückhaltend.
Poco ritenuto.

Brangæna.

(She puts the royal mantle on Isolda without her noticing it)

Un - - sel' - ge! Auf! Hört, wo wir sind!
Come, wretch - ed pair! See where we are!

sehr kräftig
fortissimo

f

All the Men (on board ship)
Tenor.

Etwas breiter im Zeitmass.
Poco allargando il tempo.

Heil!_____ Heil!_____ Heil! Kö - nig Mar-ke Heil!
Hail!_____ Hail!_____ Hail! to King Mark all hail!

Bass.

più f

ff

Kö - nig Mar - ke Heil! Heil!_____ Heil_____
Hail to Mark, the King! Hail!_____ Hail_____

3 3 3 3

f

Kurvenal (entering briskly)

Heil, Tri - stan!
Hail, Tris - tan!

dem Kö - - - nig!
our mon - - - arch!

Glück - li-cher Held!
For - tu-nate Knight!

Heil Kö - nig Mar - ke!
Hail to King Mark, O!

Mit rei - chem Hof-ge-
Surround - ed by his

sin - de, dort auf Na - chen naht Herr Mar - ke.
court - iers, in a shal - lop comes King Mark now!

Hei! wie die Fahrt ihn freut, dass er die Braut
Glad - ly he makes his way un - to his bride

acceler.

Tristan (looking up confused)

sich freit!
this day!

Wer naht?
Who comes?

Kurvenal.

Tristan. (Kurvenal points over the side)

Der Kö - - nig! Wel - cher Kö - nig?
The King, Sire! King? What King, then!

All the Men (waving their hats)
Tenor.

(Tristan gazes blankly towards the shore)

Heil! Kö - nig Mar - ke Heil! Kö - nig Mar - ke Heil!
Hail to King Mark, all hail! Hail to Mark, the King!

Bass.

ff

ff

Ped.

✳

Wieder etwas bewegter.
Poco più animato, come prima.

Isolda (in confusion)

Brangæna.

Was ist, Bran - gä - ne? Wel - cher Ruf? I - sol - de!
What's this, Bran - gæ - na? Why these cheers? I - sol - da!

p

cresc. - - -

Isolda.
B.
I.
Her-rin! Fas-sung nur heut'! Wo bin ich? Leb' ich? Ha! wel-cher
Mis-tress! For once be calm! Where am I? Live I? Ah! which the
Brangæna (with despair)
(Isolda stares in terror at Tristan)
Trank? Der Lie-bes-trank!
draught? Of Love that draught
più f
Isolda.
Tri-stan! Muss ich
Tris-tan! Must I
Tristan.
T.
I-sol-de!
I-sol-da!
ff
f
(She sinks fainting on his breast)
le-ben?
live, then?
Brangæna (to the women)
Helft der Her-rin!
Mind your Mis-tress!
più f

Gents on balcony

Tristan.

O Won - ne vol - ler Tü - cke! O trug - ge - weih - - tes
O joy with false-ness freighted! O bliss fraud - con - - se -

(People have climbed aboard; others have rigged a gangway; their behavior indicates
their expectation of the coming arrival)

Glücke!
crat-ed!

All the Men. Tenor.

(General outburst Korn - wall Heil! _____
of rejoicing) Corn - wall hail! _____

Bass.

(Trumpets on the Stage)

(The Curtain falls quickly)

Act II.
Introduction.

sehr zart
p dolciss.
pp
sehr ausdrucksvoll
molto espress.
p
poco a poco cresc.
p molto cresc.
ff
sempre ff
p

più p

poco a poco cresc.

molto cresc.

ff

sempre ff

ff

ff

ff

ff

(The Curtain rises.)

dim.

p

Scene I.

(A garden with high trees before the chamber of Isolda, which lies at one side and is approached by steps. Bright and inviting summer night. A torch burns by the open door. A hunter's horn is heard. Brangæna, standing on the steps, is watching the retreating hunt, which can still be heard)

(Horns on the Stage.)

(Brangæna looks anxiously into the chamber where she sees Isolda coming)

(Isolda with heated excitement advances from the chamber) **Isolda.**

ausdrucksvoll
espressivo

Hörst du sie noch? Mir__
Canst hearthemstill? Long__

più cresc.

__ schwand schon fern der Klang.
__ since I lost the sound.

Brangæna (listening).

Noch__sind sie nah';
Nay!__still they're near!

deut - lich
One__ can

(On the Stage.)

tönt's da-hei.
hear the horns.

dim. sempre

(Isolda listens)

pp

Isolda.

sehr zart
dolciss.

Sor - gen-de Furcht be-irrt dein Ohr;
Fear - someness makes thine ear to err;

più p

sempre pp

dich täuscht des Lau - bes säu-selnd Ge-
by rust - ling branch - es art thou mis-

tön, das la - chend schüt - telt der
led, that wav - ing, laugh in the

pp

pp

Brangæna.

Wind.
wind.

Dich täuscht des Wun - sches Un - ge-stüm zu ver-in-to
'Tis you whose wish - es wild de - ceive

molto cresc.

fp

cresc.

neh - men, was du wähnst.
hear - ing what you will.

(She listens)

f

dim.

Ich hö - re der Hör - ner Schall.
The horns, I can hear them still.

p

più p

pp

Ped.

(Isolda listens)

pp

✳

Isolda.

Nicht Hör - ner-schall tönt so
Not note of horn rings so

hold; des Quel-les sanft rie-seln-de Wel-le rauscht so
sweet. The wa-ter I hear in the well there, flow-ing

won - nig da - her. Wie hört' ich sie, tos'-ten noch
soft - ly a - way. If horns still blew, how could I

Hör-ner? Im Schwei - - gen der
hear it? In si - - lence at

Nacht nur lacht mir der Quell:
night a lone sings the well.

der mei - ner harrt in
My lov'd one waits in

zart dolce
p
pp

I.
schwei- - gen- - der Nacht, als ob
si - - lence of night. As if
pp
cresc.
Hör- - ner noch nah' dir schallten, willst du ihn fern
horns were as yet in hear-ing, wouldst thou pre-vent
f dim.
p
cresc.
ff
I.
B.
Brangæna.
mir hal-ten? Der dei- ner
his nearing? Thy lov- er
ff
p
molto cresc.
B.
harrt, o hör' mein War- nen! dess' har-ren
waits: O hear my warn - ing! there lurks a
f
f
B.
Spä-her zur Nacht. Weil du er-blindet, wähnst du den Blick der Welt er-
spy here by night. And, be thou blinded, wit you, the eyes of all are
p
p
p

114

blö-det für euch?
watching on you!

Da dort an Schiffes Bord, von Tristan's
That day when there on board, from Tristan's

be - ben-der Hand, die blei-che Braut, kaum ih-rer mächtig, Kö-nig Mar-ke em-
trem - u-lous hands King Mark received his fair-ly fainting, pale and pas-sion-less

pfing,
bride:

als Al-les ver-wirrt auf die Wan-ken-de sah, der güt'-ge
when all were a-ghast and were gaz-ing on thee, the gracious

Kö - nig, mild be - sorgt, die Mü-hen der lan-gen Fahrt, die du
mon - arch's kind con-cern to wear-i-ness of the way thou hadst

lit-test, laut be-klagt:— ein Einz'ger war's, ich ach-tet' es wohl,—
journeyed, laid the blame. But one there was— I not-ed it well,—

18325

der nur Tri-stan fasst' ins Au-ge;
who had eyes_for Tris-tan on-ly;

mit bös-li-cher List,
with hostile de-sign

lau-ern-dem Blick sucht' er in sei-ner Mie-ne zu fin-den, was ihm
low-er'd his look; so did he then ob-serve him, to find what-e'er might

poco cresc.

poco riten. *a tempo*

die-ne. Tückisch lauschend treff' ich ihn oft:_ der heimlich euch um-
serve him. Fur-tive list'ning find I him oft; some plot he would pre-

p *cresc.*

garnt, vor Me-lot seid ge-warnt!
pare: Of Me-lot, then, be-ware!

f *p* *p*

Isolda.

Meinst du Herrn Me-lot?
Mean'st thou Sir Me-lot?

O, wie du dich
How art thou de-

più p

116

trügst! Ist es nicht Tri-stan's treu-e-ster Freund? Muss mein
ceived! Is he not Tris-tan's faith-ful-lest friend? When my

Trau--ter mich mei--den, dann weilt er bei
lov--er must leave me, he lin-gers with

Brangæna.

Me-lot al-lein. Was mir ihn ver-dächtig, macht dir ihn
Me-lot a-lone. For what I distrust him, to thee he's

theu-er! Von Tristan zu Mar-ke ist Me-lot's Weg; dort
dear-er! From Tristan to Mark 'tis, that Me-lot goes; there

sä't er üb-le Saat. Die heut' im Rath dies nächtli-che
sows he e-vil seed. And those who now this e-ven-ing

18325

Ja-gen so ei - lig schnell be-schlossen, einem edlern Wild, als dein Wähnen
hunting arranged with so much hur - ry, 'tis a high-er game, than you wit, they

meint, gilt ih - re Jä - gers - list.
deem worthy their hunts - man - ship.

Isolda.

Dem Freund zu
For friend - ship's

zart
p *dolce*
Red.

Lieb' er-fand die - se List ___ aus Mit - leid
sake ___ the plan was de - vised; ___ so helps Sir

zart
dol.
Red.

Me - lot, der Freund. Nun willst du den Treu - en
Me - lot his friend. Now wouldst thou this friend - ship

p *poco a poco cresc. -*

schel - ten? Bes - ser als du ___ sorgt er für mich;
slan - der? Bet - ter than thou ___ cares he for me!

cresc.
f

ihm öff - net er, was mir du sperrst. O spa - re
He opes to me what thou wouldst bar. Ah! spare the

cresc. - molto cresc. - - più f

mir des Zö - gerns Noth!__ Das Zei - - chen,
pain of more__ de - lay!__ The sig - - nal,

f

Brangä - ne! O gieb das Zei - chen! Lö - sche des
Brangæ - na! O give the sig - nal! Out with the

p *f* *p* *f*

Lich - - tes letz - - - - ten
light's - last lin - - - - - g'ring

p *f* *p*

Schein! Dass ganz sie sich nei - ge,
flame! That now she come nigh us,

f *dim. - - - -*

win - ke der Nacht! Schon
bid we the night! E'en

goss sie ihr Schwei - - gen durch
now steals her si - - lence o'er

p

più p *pp*

Hain und Haus, schon
house and haw, e'en

füllt sie das Herz mit won - ni - gem
now feels my heart her rap - tur - ous

pp

Graus. O lö - sche das Licht nun
awe. Oh! quench me the light at

poco cresc. -

I. aus,/last!

lö - sche den scheu - chenden/Quench _____ me its fear - bringing

I. Schein!/flame!

Lass'/Time

mei - nen Lieb - - - sten/'tis,_ my lov'd _____

sten/one

I.
B. Brangæna.

ein!/came!

O lass'/O leave

die warn - nen-de/the light with its

Zün-de!/warn-ing!

lass'/Leave

B. die Ge - fahr/it to point

sie dir/to thy

zei-gen!/per - il!

O/Ah,

B. we — he! We — he! Ach mir
woe's me! Woe's me! Poor, poor

B. Ar — men! Des un-se-li-gen Tran-kes!
peo — ple! That love-po-tion un-ho-ly!

Ein wenig mässiger im Zeitmass.
Poco meno mosso.

B. Dass ich un-treu ein-mal nur der Her-rin Wil-len trog! Ge-
That I faith-less was, for once, my la-dy to de-fraud! Had

B. horcht' ich taub und blind, dein Werk war dann der Tod:
I stood deaf and blind, thy work had been thy death:

B. doch, dei-ne Schmach, dei — ne
but thy dis-grace and thy

schmäh - lich - ste Noth, mein Werk muss ich
great - est of griefs, my work I as_

Wieder lebhafter im Zeitmass.
Più animato come prima.

Isolda.

Schuld' - ge es wis-sen! Dein Werk? O thör'ge
guilt - y must own it! Thy work! O fool-ish

molto cresc.

poco rall.

Magd! Frau Min - ne kenn - test du nicht? Nicht_ ihres
maid! Know'st not the god - dess of love? know'st not her

poco rall.

p cresc. *zart*
p dolce

Ein wenig mässiger als zuvor.
Poco più moderato ancora.

zart
dolce

Zau - bers Macht? Des kühn - sten Mu - thes
won - drous pow'r? Of keen - est quests is

mf

Kö - ni-gin? des Wel - ten-wer - dens Wal - te-rin?
she the queen! She works for what the world will be!

p

f

Le - - - ben und Tod sind
Life _____ and death are

un - - ter-than ihr, die sie
sub - - ject to her, these she

webt _____ aus _____ Lust _____ und Leid,
weaves _____ of _____ joy _____ and woe:

in _____ Lie - - be wan -
and _____ love _____ from en -

- delnd _____ den Neid. Des To - des Werk,
- vy _____ to flow. The work of death

nahm ich's vermessen zur Hand,
I rash-ly took to my hand;

Frau
Love's

Min - - ne hat es mei - ner Macht ent -
god - - dess un - to me did coun - ter -

wandt. Die Tod - ge - weih - te nahm sie in Pfand, fass - te das Werk in ih - re
mand. Death's vic - tims then she took as her own; now by her hand the work be

Sehr zurückhaltend.
Molto ritardando.

Mässig bewegt.
Moderato con moto.

Hand. Wie sie es wen - det,
done! Wher - e'er she guides it,

wie sie es en - det, was sie mir küh - re,
how she de - cides it, what rood she reads me,

wo - hin mich füh - re, ihr ward ich zu
where - so she leads me, she on - ly doth
p
p
p
cresc.
poco riten.
ei - gen: nun lass mich ge - hor - sam
own me: so have I o - be - dient
poco riten.
f
f
p
Lebhafter bewegt.
Più vivace.
Brangæna.
zei - gen! Und muss - te der Min - ne tü - ckischer
shown me! Yet e'en tho'you drank that dire - ful-lest
Sehr bewegt.
Molto animato.
f
p
Trank des Sin - nes Licht dir ver - lö - schen, darfst du nicht
draught, the light of sense to be - smother, may you not
cresc.
se - hen, wenn ich dich war - ne: nur heu - te hör', o
lis - ten, now, when I warn you? For once, I beg, ah,

B.
hör' mein Fle - hen! Der Ge-fahr leuch - ten-des Licht,
do my bid - ding! Danger yet looks from the light:
nur heu - te, heut! die
this once, this once! Quench
Immer bewegter.
Sempre più mosso.
B.
I.
Isolda.
Fa - ckel dort lö - sche nicht! Die im Bu - sen
not the torch for to - night! She that kin - dles
f
dim.
p
f
meno f
I.
mir die Gluth ent - facht,
thus my soul's de - sire,
p
cresc.
I.
die mir das Her - ze bren - nen
she that my heart has set on

macht, die mir als Tag der
fire, whose smile for me is

See — — le — lacht, Frau Min — — ne
sun — — shine bright, Love's god — — dess

sempre f

will, es wer — — de Nacht,
wills, it now be night,

più f

dass hell sie dor ten
that dark — — ness there may

ff

(as she hastens toward the torch)

leuch — te, wo sie dein
van — ish, where her thy

dim.

(She takes the torch from the doorway)

Licht ver-scheuchte. Zur War-te du: dort wa-che treu! Die
light doth banish. Go thou on guard, and watch thou well! The

p *cresc.*

Leuch - - te, und wär's meines Le-bens Licht,
torch_____ here, and were it my light of life,

f *p trem.*

lach - - end sie zu lö-schen zag' ich
smil - - ing I should quench it, with - out

f *p trem.*

(She throws the torch to the ground, where it gradually goes out)

nicht!
strife.

ff

(Brangæna turns distressedly away in order to get upon the roof by an outer staircase,

where she slowly disappears)

(Isolda listens and looks, at first timidly, down the avenue of trees)

(Stirred by increasing longing, she goes nearer to the avenue and looks out more boldly)

dolce

(She waves her kerchief, at first from time to

cresc.

time, then oftener, finally with passionate impatience, faster and faster.)

sempre con 𝒫ed.

18325

Immer bewegter.
Sempre più animato.

(A gesture of sudden delight shows that she has perceived her lover in the

distance. She raises herself higher and higher, the better to overlook the place, then hurries back

to the steps, from the top of which she beckons to him as he approaches)

Scene II.
Tristan and Isolda.

più f

Tristan (rushing in)

I - sol - - - de!
I - sol - - - da!

ff

ff

Isolda.

Tri - - stan! Ge - lieb - - ter!
Tris - - tan! Be - lov - - ed!

Ge - lieb - - te!
Be - lov - - ed!

(Embracing wildly,

f

più f

ff

ff

they come down the stage)

sempre immer f

fff

18325

Sehr lebhaft.
Molto vivace.
(♪ schneller als zuvor ♪) (Das Zeitmass ist je nach dem feurigeren oder zärtlichen Ausdruck gut zu mo-
(♪ quicker than the preceding ♪)(The tempo must follow the expression, now ardent, now tender.)   [tiviren.]

Isolda.
Bist du mein?   Darf ich dich fas-sen!
Art thou mine?   Can I then hold thee?

Tristan.
Hab'ich dich wie-der?   Kann ich mir
Have I then got thee?   Can I be-

End-lich! End-lich!   Fühl'ich dich wirk-lich?
At last, then! At last, then!   Is't true I touch thee?

trau-en?   An mei-ner Brust!   Seh' ich dich
lieve it?   Here on my heart!   See I thy-

Dies dei-ne Au-gen?   Hier dei-ne Hand?
Are these thine eyes?   Here thy___ hand?

sel-ber?   Dies dein Mund?   Hier dein___
self, dear?   This thy mouth?   Here thy___

I.
Bin ___ ich's? Bist du's? Halt' ich dich fest?
Is't ___ I? Is't thou? Have I thee fast?

T.
Herz? Bin ich's? Bist du's? Ist es kein Trug?_
heart? Is't I? Is't thou? Is it no trick?_

accel. *molto accel.*

I.
Ist es kein Traum?_____ O
Is it no dream?_____ O

T.
molto accel.
Ist es kein Traum?_____ O
Is it no dream?_____ O

accel.

p *molto cresc.* - - - -

(Die ♩ wie zuvor im ²⁄₂.)
(*The* ♩ *as before in* ²⁄₂.)

I.
Won - - - - - ne der See - - le, o
joy _____ of my be - - ing! O

T.
Won - - - - - ne der See - - le, o
joy _____ of my be - - ing! O

ff

f

I. süsse, hehr-ste, kühn-ste, schön-ste, se-lig-ste Lust! _____
sweet-est, high-est, rare-est, fair-est, ho-li-est joy! _____

T. süsse, hehr-ste, kühn-ste, schön-ste, se-lig-ste Lust!___ Oh-ne Glei-che!
sweet-est, high-est, rare-est, fair-est, ho-li-est joy!___ More than trea-sure!

p

cresc. _ _

I. Ü-ber-rei-che! E-wig! Un-ge-ahn-te,
With-out mea-sure! End-less! Longed-for ev-er,

T. Ü-ber-se-lig! E-wig!
Glor-ious,bound-less, end-less!

I. nie ge-kann-te!
known _ of nev-er!

T. Ü-berschwäng-lich hoch er-
O-ver-whelm-ing sub-li-

I.

Freu - de - jauch - - zen! Him - - mel -
Heart - up - heav - - ing! Heav - - en's ___

T.

hab' - ne! Lust - ent - zü - cken!
ma - tion! Love - re - li - ant,

I.

höch - stes ___ Welt - ent - rü - - - - -
high - est, ___ earth - de - fi - - - - -

T.

Him - mel - höch - stes Welt - ent - rü - - - - -
Heav - en's high - est, earth - de - fi - - - - -

più f

I.

cken! Mein! ___
ant! Mine! ___

T.

cken! Mein! ___
ant! Mine! ___

più f

ff

I.
Tri - stan mein!
Tris - tan mine!
T.
I - sol - de
I - sol - da
f
I.
Tri-stan mein!
Tris-tan mine!
Mein und dein!
Mine and thine!
T.
mein! I - sol - de mein!
mine! I - sol - da mine!
Mein und dein!
Mine and thine!
fp
fp
fp
più f
I.
E - wig! Tri - stan mein, I - sol - de e - wig
Al - ways! Tris - tan mine, I - sol - da al - ways
T.
E - wig! I-
Al - ways! I-
fff
3
Ped.
Ped.
Ped.
Ped.

I.
dein!   Tri - stan!   Tri - stan!
thine!   Tris - tan!   Tris - tan!

T.
sol - de mein! ___   I-sol - de!   I-sol - de!
sol - da mein! ___   I-sol - da!   I-sol - da!

con Ped.

I.
E - - - wig, ___ e - - - wig
Al - - - ways, ___ al - - - ways

T.
E - - - wig, ___ e - - - wig
Al - - - ways, ___ al - - - ways

cresc. -

I.
ein! _____
thine! _____

T.
ein! _____
thine! _____

ff   ff

I. Wie lan - ge fern! Wie fern so_ lang!
How long a - far! How far so_ long!

T. Wie weit so
How far, so

T. I. nah'! So nah'_ wie weit! O Freun - des - fein - din, bö - se
near! So near,_ how far! O foe to friend - ship, dread - ful

Isolda.

I. Fer - ne! Trä - ger Zei - ten zö - gernde Län-ge!
dis - tance! Wretch - ed hours of wear - i-some wait-ing!

Tristan

T. O Weit' und Nä - he! hart ent - zwei - te!
But far, or near thee, sep - a - ra - tion!

140

T. Hol - - de Nä - - he! Ö - de Wei - - te!
Pre - - cious pres - - ence! Dread - ful dis - - tance!

p *cresc.*

Isolda.

I. Im Dun - kel du, im Lich - - te ich!
In dark - ness thou, in light I lived!

f *dim.* *p*

Tristan.

T. Das Licht! Das Licht! O die-ses Licht, wie
The light! The light! O yet that light, how

f p f p f dim.

T. lang' verlosch es nicht! Die Son-ne sank, der Tag ver-
long 'twas there in sight! The sun went down, the day was

p cresc. p dolce

T. ging, doch sei-nen Neid erstickt' er nicht: sein scheu-chend Zei-chen zün-det er
done; yet was its hate-ful light not hid: the warn-ing sig-nal kept it a-

p f f

18325

T.
an und steckt's an der Lieb - sten Thü - re, dass nicht ich zu ihr
glow be - side my love's door on fire, — so I could not come

p   *f*   *dim.* —

T. / I. **Isolda.**
füh - re. Doch der Lieb - sten Hand lösch - te das Licht; wess' die
nigh - er. Yet thy dear one's hand dark - ened it here; what my

p dolce

I.
Magd sich wehr - te, scheut' ich mich nicht: in Frau
maid re - fused me, I did not fear: since on

p   *ausdrucksvoll espressivo*   *cresc.*

I.
Min - ne's Macht und Schutz, bot ich dem Ta - ge
love I may re - ly, day - light do I de -

f   *p*   *cresc.*   *f*   *dim.*   *p cresc.*

Heftig drängend im Zeitmass.
Stringendo veemente.

I. / T. **Tristan.**
Trutz! Dem Ta - ge: dem Ta - ge!
fy! The day - - light! The day - - light!

f   *3*

Immer sehr schnell.
Sempre molto presto.

T. dem tü - cki - schen Ta - ge, dem
With treach - er - y freight - ed, our

T. här - te - sten Fein - de Hass und
bit - ter - est foe, so feared and

T. Kla - ge! Wie du das
hat - ed! As with this

T. Licht, o könnt' ich die Leuch - te, der
link, I'd deal with all day - light, our

T. Lie - be Lei - den zu rä - chen, dem frechen Ta - ge ver-
lov - ing long - ings a - veng - ing, the gar - ish day-light by

T.
lö-schen! Giebt's ei-ne Noth, giebt's ei-ne Pein, die er nichtweckt mit seinem
quenching! Is there a grief, is there a care that's not a-wak-en'd by its

Sehr schnell.
Molto presto.
Ein wenig zurückhaltend.
Poco ritenuto.

T.
Schein? Selbst in der Nacht däm — mern-der
glare? E'en in the night, dawn, break — ing

Erste Bewegung.
Tempo primo.

T.
Pracht hegt ihn Lieb-chen am Haus, streckt mir dro-hend ihn
bright, to thy cham-ber doth hie, from whose threats I must

Isolda.

T.
I.
aus! Hegt' ihn die Lieb-ste am eig'-nen Haus, —
fly! And if the light to my house do hie, —

Sehr lebhaft.
Molto vivace.

I.
im eig'-nen Her-zen hell und kraus hegt' ihn trot-zig einst mein Trau-ter,
with-in thy heart did light not lie, in the days when thou, my lov-er,

poco riten.   **a tempo**

Tri - stan,   der mich be - trog!   War's nicht   der
Tris - tan,   didst play   me false?   Was't not   the

poco riten.   *a tempo*

f   *p*   *p ausdrucksvoll*
                espressivo

Tag,   der aus ihm log,   als er nach Ir - land wer - bend zog,   für
light   for which he lied,   when he sought Ire - land for   a bride,   to

f   *p*   *f*   *dim.*   *p cresc.* —

Mar - ke mich _____ zu frei'n, _____ dem Tod die Treu - e zu
woo for Mark, _____ the King, _____ to death his dear - est to

riten.

f   *f*   *ff*   *dim.*

riten.

a tempo   **Tristan.**

weih'n?   Der   Tag!   Der Tag, der dich um -
bring?   The   Light!   The Light that round thee

ff a tempo   *ff*   *f*

gliss,   da - hin, wo sie der Son - ne glich,   in höchster Eh - ren
shone,   for this, that as the sun's   it - self,   with hon-our's brightest

più f   *ff*   *p*   *cresc.*   *ff*

Glanz und Licht, I - sol - den mir ent - rückt'! Was mir das
ray and light it barr'd I - sold' from me! What my en-

Au - ge so ent - zückt', mein Her - ze tief zur
tranc - ed eyes might see, my heart must crush to

Er - de drückt': in lich - ten Ta - ges Schein wie
earth for thee: For while that light should shine, how

war I - sol - de mein? War sie nicht
might I - sold' be mine? Was she not

Isolda.

dein, die dich er - kor? Was
thine, when thee I chose? What

(Der Bass möglichst gehalten.)
(Il basso molto tenuto.)

18325

I.
log der bö-se Tag dir_ vor, dass, die für dich be-schie-den, die Traute du ver-
lies could e-vil day dis-close, that thoucouldst so be-tray me, that was to thee so

f   *p*   *f*   *dim.*   *p*

Red.   ✱   Red.   ✱

I.
T.
Tristan.
rie - thest?   Was dich um - gliss mit
loy - al?   What - e'er en - hanced thy

cresc.   *f* *sehr feurig con molto fuoco*   *più f*

T.
hehr - ster_ Pracht,   der Eh - re
beau - ty bright,   thine hon - our

f   *più f*

T.
Glanz,   des_ Ruh - - mes Macht, an sie meinHerz zu hangen,hielt
pure,   thy_ fame,   thy might, forthese to fight for ev-er, was

ff   *dim.*   *p*

T.
mich der Wahn ge - fan-gen.   Die   mit des
then my false en - deav-or.   Then   did the

più p   *p*   *cresc.*

T. Schimmers hell - stem Schein mir Haupt und Schei-tel licht _ be -
shin - ing sun that shed its rays a - - round my brain _ and _

T. schien, der Wel-ten-Eh-ren Ta - - ges -
head, with world-ly hon-our's day - - light _

accel.

T. Son - ne, mit ih - rer Strah - - len
mea - sure, with all its splen - - did,
accel.

Allmählich zurückhaltend.
Poco a poco ritardando.

T. eit - - ler Won - - ne, durch Haupt und
emp - - ty plea - - sure, through head and

T. Schei-tel drang mir ein, bis _ in des Her - zens tief - sten
brain of me did dart, down _ to my deep - est depth of

18325

Schrein. / heart.

Was dort in keu-scher Nacht / What shy-ly wrapp'd in night

dun-kel verschlossen / lurked hid-den from my

wacht', was oh-ne Wiss'und Wahn ich dämmernd dort em-pfah'n: / sight unknown and un-ex-press'd, I had but dim-ly guess'd,

p dolce

pp

p dolce

più p

ein Bild,_____ das meine Au - gen zu schau'n sich nicht ge- / a vi - - sion that I nev - er had dared to gaze on

pp

pp dolce

Etwas belebend. / Poco animando

trauten, von des Ta - ges Schein be - troffen lag mir's da schimmernd / ev-er, by the day-light's beams dis-cover'd, blazed forth and lay un-

p / *p poco cresc.*

Schnell belebend. / Accelerando subito.

Wieder ganz belebt. / Vivace, come prima.

of-fen. Was mir so rühmlich schien und hehr, das rühmt' ich hell vor_ / cover'd. Then all I held so high and fair,_ to all the world did_

p cresc.

più cresc.

f *p*

T. al - lem Heer; vor al - lem Vol - ke pries ich laut der
I de - clare, to all man-kind thy praise I cried as

cresc. *f* *p* *cresc.*

T. Er - de schön - ste Kö - nigs
Earth's most fair and queen - ly

f *più f* *ff*

Immer sehr lebhaft.
Sempre molto vivace.

T. Braut. Dem Neid, den mir der Tag er-
bride. The hate this day-light did

kräftig gestossen
staccato con forza

ff *più f*

T. weckt'; dem Ei-fer, den mein Glü - cke schreckt'; der
wake, the en-vy that my peace could shake, the

f *p* *cresc.*

T. Missgunst, die mir Eh - ren und Ruhm be-gann zu schwe-ren:
cov - et - ous fore-bod-ing that hon-our was cor-rod-ing:

f *p* *cresc.* *sf cresc.*

T.

de-nen bot ich Trotz, und treu be-schloss, um Ehr' und Ruhm zu
All did I de - fy, and tru-ly_ try my name and fame to_

T.

wah - ren, nach_ Ir - land ich zu fah - - -
save_ me; 'twas_ this to Ire - land drave

più f

Sehr schnell.
Allegro molto. Isolda.

T.
I.

ren. O eit - ler Ta - gesknecht!
me. O day - light's fu - tile dupe!

ff

ff

ff

dim.

p

Immer noch sehr bewegt.
Sempre molto vivace.

I.

Ge - täuscht_ von ihm, der dich_ ge-täuscht, wie musst'ich lie - bend um dich
De - ceived_ by what de - ceiv - ed thee, long did I suf - fer, tho' I

sehr ausdrucksvoll
molto espressivo

p

I. leiden, den, in des Tages falschem Pran - gen, von seines
loved thee! For, whilethe day-light falsely glit - ter'd, was I by

cresc. *f* *p*

I. Glei - ssens Trug be - fan - gen, dort,_____ wo ihn Lie - - be heiss um-
flar - ing fraud en - fet - ter'd! Where_____ in my heart_____ warm love a-

f *p* *ausdrucksvoll espressivo* *p cresc. -*

I. fass - te, im tiefsten Her - zen hell ich hass - te.
wait - ed, with-in my hot - test heart I hat - ed!

molto cresc. - *ff* *ff*

ff *dim.*

Sehr lebhaft.
Molto vivace.

I. Ach, in des Her - zens Grun - de, wie schmerz - te tief die
Ah! when my heart_____ was break-ing, how deep the wound was

sf *p* *sf* *molto cresc. -*

I. Wun - de! Den __ dort ich heim - lich barg,
ach ing!
To __ him I did con - ceal,

I. wie dünkt' er mich so arg, wenn in des Ta - ges Schei - ne der
how bit - ter did I feel; when in the day - light's splen - dor, the

I. treu ge - heg - te Ei - ne der Lie - be Bli - cken schwand, als Feind
lov - ing looks and ten - der that mine had been, were gone, a foe

I. nur vor mir stand! Das als Ver - rä - ther dich mir wies, dem Licht des
seemed he a - lone! Light, that had made you false to me, the light of

I. Ta - ges wollt' ich ent - flieh'n, dort - hin in die Nacht __ dich mit mir zieh'n,
day, I thought I would flee, and far in the night __ drag thee with me,

Ein wenig mässiger, doch immer noch bewegt.
Un poco più moderato, ma sempre animato.
I.
wo der Täu - schung En - - - de mein Herz mir ver-
where my heart had told me, de - lu - sion would
p
f
hiess, wo des Trug's ge - ahn - - ter Wahn zer -
die, where de - ceit and fear should en - - ter
p
dim.
più p
pp
Etwas zurückhaltend.
Poco ritenuto.
(zart)
(dolce)
rin - - ne; dort dir zu trin - ken ew' - ge Min - ne, mit
nev - - er; there had I pledged thee love for ev - er, I
p
Wieder weniger zurückhaltend.
Meno ritenuto.
mir dich im Ver - ein wollt' ich dem To - - de
wished, thou, joined with me, pledged un - to death mightst
poco cresc.
mf
dim.
più p
Sehr belebend.
Molto animando.
Tristan.
I.
T.
weih'n. In dei - ner Hand den sü - ssen
be. When I per - ceived what you had
p molto cresc.
f
p

T.
Tod, als ich ihn er-kannt, den sie mir bot; als mir die
planned, that you held my death with-in your hand, when I had
cresc.
Ah-nung hehr und ge-wiss zeig-te, was mir die Süh-ne ver-
clear-ly guessed your in-tent, what by your prom-ised par-don was
più cresc.
hiess: da er-däm-merte mild er-hab-ner
meant, then there dawned in my heart a ten-der
più f
ff
dim.
p
pp
Macht im Bu-sen mir die Nacht; mein Tag war
might, that came to me from night: my day then
cresc.
f dim.
Isolda.
T.
I.
da vollbracht. Doch ach, dich täusch-te der fal-sche Trank, dass dir von
lost its light. But ah! that draught, it de-ceived thee, too, wrest-ing thee
fp
fp

I.

Neu - em die Nacht ver-sank: dem   ein - zig am To - de
then from the night a - new: and   those who a - dy - ing

cresc.

p

Etwas zögernd.   Sehr belebt.
Poco rall.   Molto animato.   Tristan.

I.
T.

lag,   den gab er wie-der dem Tag!   O
lay,   once more were giv-en to day!   All

poco cresc.   *molto cresc.*

T.

Heil   dem   Tran - ke!
hail   the   po - tion!

f   *p*   *cresc.*

T.

Heil _____ sei - nem Saft!   Heil _____
Hail _____ to its power!   Hail _____

f   *p* *molto cresc.*   *f*

T.

- sei - nes Zau - - bers heh - - rer
to its ma - - gic might in that

p cresc.

Kraft! / hour!

Durch des To - -des / Through the door of

Thor, _____ wo er mir floss, / death _____ when flowed its tide,

weit und of - - - - -fen er mir er - tals / lo, it o - - - - -pen'd those por - tals

schloss, da - rin ich sonst nur / wide, of realms till then but

träu- -mend ge - wacht, das Won- - -ne - / dreams in my sight, the glo - -rious

T. reich der Nacht. Von dem Bild in des
realms of night. On the face that my

T. Her- zens ber- -gen-dem Schrein scheucht' er des
heart so deep did en-shrine, nev-er a-

Immer mehr belebend.
Sempre più animando.

T. Ta- -ges täuschenden Schein, dass nacht-sich-tig mein Au- -ge
gain false daylight could shine: nor keep Tristan un-du- -ly

accel.

Lebhaft.
Vivace.

T. wahr es zu se- -hen tau- -ge.
from see-ing all things tru- -ly.

a tempo

Immer lebhafter.
Più vivace.

Isolda.

I. Doch es räch- -te sich der ver-scheuch- -te
But the light was an- ger'd to be thus

18325

I. Tag; mit dei-nen Sün-den Rath's er pflag: was dir ge-
banned; and with thy sins went hand in hand: What thou didst

I. zeigt die däm-mern-de Nacht, an des
learn in twi-light of night, thou didst

I. Tag-Ge-stir-nes Kö-nigs-macht
soon for-get in king-ly light,

Sehr schnell.
Molto presto.

I. muss-test du's ü-ber-ge-ben, um
and my love didst sur-ren-der, to

schleppend
strascinante

I. ein-sam in ö-der Pracht schimmernd dort zu le-
live all a-lone in bright realms of des-ert splen-

Viel langsamer werdend.
Molto lentando.

Wieder lebhaftes Zeitmass.
Tempo primo. Vivace.

I.

ben.___
dor.

Wie er-trug_ ich's nur?
How en-dure_ it, then?

Wie er-trag' ich's noch?
How en-dure it, now?

Sehr feurig.
Con molto fuoco.

Tristan.

T.

O,___ nun wa-ren wir Nacht-___ -ge-en-
O,___ now were we by night___ en-

T.

weih-___ -te!
chant-___ -ed,

Der tü-cki-sche Tag, der Neid-be-
the trouble-some day, with en-vy

(sehr ausdrucksvoll)
(molto espressivo)

T.

rei-te, tren-nen konnt' uns sein Trug,
haunt-ed, part us might with its lies,

doch nicht mehr täu-
but nev-er daz-

T.

schen sein Lug!
zle our eyes!

Sei-ne eit-le Pracht,
For its emp-ty glare,

T. sei-nen prah - len-den Schein ver - lacht, wem die Nacht den
and its glit - ter-ing light, are flout - ed by all that

T. Blick ge - weiht: sei-nes fla-ckernden Lich - tes flüchti - ge
love the night. For its flick-er - ing beams, so fit-ful-ly

T. Blit-ze blen - - den uns nicht mehr. Wer des To - - des
flashing, blind our eyes no more. Who the night of

T. Nacht lie-bend er-schaut, wem sie ihr tief Ge-heim-niss ver-
death lov-ing-ly scan, those who have gazed on her se - - cret

T. traut: des Ta - ges Lü - gen, Ruhm und Ehr', Macht und Ge-
plan, will hold false day-light's rank and name, hon - our and

T. winn, so schimmernd hehr, wie eit- ler Staub der Son- nen sind sie vor dem zer-
pow'r and wealth and fame, as mere-ly dust that drift-eth, and through the sun- light

cresc. *fp* *f dim.*

T. sponnen!
sift-eth!

pp

T. In des Ta- -ges eit- -lem Wäh- -nen
When the day is bright- ly burn- ing,

cresc.

T. bleibt ihm ein ein- -zig Seh- -nen, das
naught is there left but yearn- -ing. Bid

accel.
accèl.
molto cresc.

Etwas gedehnt.
Poco steso.

T. Seh-nen hin zur heil'- gen Nacht, wo ur-e-wig, ein-zig wahr,
yearning hence to ho- ly night, where, ev- er and on-ly true,

ff *ff*

18325

Langsamer, und allmählich immer langsamer.
Rallentando sempre poco a poco.

Lie - bes - won - ne ihm lacht.
love and pas - sion in - vite!

(Tristan draws Isolda gently down

on a flowery bank at one side, sinks on his knees before her and rests his head on her arm)

Mässig langsam.
Lento moderato.

Isolda.

O De-

Tristan.

O sink' her-nie -der, Nacht der Liebe,
De-scend up-on us, night of passion,

sink' her-nie -der, Nacht der Liebe,
scend up-on us, night of pas-sion,

Lie -be,
pas -sion,

gieb Ver-ges - sen, dass ich
let us live, our life for-

gieb Ver-ges - sen, dass ich le -be,
let us live, our life for - get -ting,

le -be,
get -ting,

nimm mich auf in dei -nen
lift, oh! lift us up to

I. nimm mich auf___ in dei-nen Schoss,
lift, __ oh, lift___ us up to thee!
lö - se von der Welt mich
from the world now set us

T. Schoss,
thee!
lö - se von der Welt mich los!
from the world now set us free!

più p
pp

I.
T. Tristan.
los! Ver - lo - schen nun die letz - - te Leuch - te;
free! For van - ished are the light's____ last gleam - ings,

pp (zart) (dolce)

Isolda.
was wir dach - -ten, was uns däuch - te;
All that daunt- -ed, all that haunt- -ed,

(zart) p (dolce)
più p

Isolda.
all' Ge - mah - -nen,
- all our grop- -ing,

Tristan.
all' Ge - den - -ken,
all our seem- -ing,

p espress.
poco cresc. -

18325

I.
heil'- -ger Dämm' - rung heh- -res
ho- -ly twi- -light's sweet- -est
T.
heil'- -ger Dämm'- -rung heh- -res Ah- -nen
ho- -ly twi- -light's sweet- -est hop- -ing,
p
poco cresc.
poco f
I.
p
Ah- -nen löscht des Wäh- -nens Graus
hop- -ing, let false fears be hurled
T.
löscht des Wäh- -nens Graus welt- -
let false fears be hurled from
cresc.
molto cresc.
Breiter.
Allargando.
Sehr breit und zurückhaltend.
Ritenuto e largo.
riten.
I.
welt- - -er-lö- - -send aus.
from a van- - -ished world.
T.
- er-lö- - -send aus.
- a van- - -ished world.
ff
dim.
p riten.

Wieder mässig langsam.
Lento moderato, come prima.

Isolda.
ruhig
p tranquillo

I.

Barg im Bu- -sen uns sich die Son- ne, leuch-ten la-
Could our hearts_ the sun but im-pris- on, laugh-ing stars_

Sehr ruhig.
Molto tranquillo.

I.

- chend Ster-he der Won- -ne.
_ of love were a-ris- -en.

Tristan.

Von dei- nem Zau- -ber sanft_ um-
While thus thy power_ is through us

T.

spon- nen, vor dei- nen Au- -gen süss zer- ron- -nen,
flow- ing, thine eyes a-bove_ us soft-ly_ glow- -ing,

immer sempre

Isolda.

I.

Herz an Herz_ dir, Mund an Mund;_
Heart to heart_ and lips to lips,_

T.

ei- nes A- -thems ein'- -ger
One the breath_ that 'twixt them

p dolce

p dolce

I.
bricht mein Blick sich wonn' - er - blin - det, er - bleicht die Welt
Breaks my glance at glo - ry blind - ing, and pales the earth
T.
Bund; bricht mein Blick sich wonn' - er - blin - det, er -
slips, breaks my glance at glo - ry blind - ing, and
p dolce
più p
I.
mit ih - rem Blen - den: die uns der Tag trü - gend er -
to ra - diance bend - ing, that once the day lit with its
T.
bleicht die Welt mit ih - rem Blen - den:
pales the earth to ra - diance bend - ing:
pp
p
helIt, selbst dann bin
lies. I then, I
zu täuschendem Wahn entge - genge - stellt, selbst dann bin
At fraud - u - lent dreams de - fi - ance I've hurled: I then, I
accel.
cresc.
Ped.

Erstes Tempo.
Tempo primo.

I. ich die Welt:_____ Won_____ ne-
am the world._____ Joy_____ life's

T. ich die Welt:_____ Won_____ ne-
am the world._____ Joy_____ life's

Erstes Tempo.
Tempo primo.

ff   dim.

Ped.

I. hehr_____ stes We-
won_____ drous weav-

p

T. hehr_____ stes We-
won_____ drous weav-

p

p

Ped.

I. ben, Lie_____ be-hei- lig- stes
ing, Love life's ho- li- est

ff

T. ben, Lie_____ be-hei- lig- stes
ing, Love life's ho- li- est

molto cresc._____ (sehr ausdrucksvoll) dim.
ff (molto espress.)

I.
T.
B.
rallent.
dim.
a tempo
p
p a tempo
Le- - - ben, Nie - wie - der - er - wa- - - - chens
liv- - - - ing: Our ne'er-re - a - wak- -ning,
Le- - - - ben, Nie - wie - der - er - wa- - - - chens
liv- - - - ing: Our ne'er-re - a - wak- - - - -ning,
piu p
pp
(ersterbend)
(morendo)
wahn - los hold be - wuss - ter Wunsch.
dream - less, long - a - wait - ed wish.
(Completely carried away, Tristan and Isolda sink down and remain lying on the flowery bank, their heads side by side)
Brangæna (from the turret, invisible)
Ein- - - - - - - -sam wa- - - - - -chend
Lone- - - - - - -ly watch I
in der Nacht,
here to- -night:
poco cresc.

wem _____ der Traum _____ der Lie- -
Ye _____ that dream _____ of love- -

- be - lacht,
- -de- -light,

ausdrucksvoll
espressivo

(gesteigert)
(appassionato)

hab' _____ der Ei - - -
let _____ your ears

ausdrucksvoll
espressivo

- -nen Ruf _____ in -
my call _____ re-

Acht, _____ die den Schlä - -fern
quite, _____ call that should your

sehr zart und ausdrucksvoll
dolcissimo e molto espressivo

B.
Schlim- - -mes ahnt, ban- - - -
slum- - -ber shake, warn- - - -
dim.
p
- - -ge zum Er- -wa- - - -
- - -ing you to fear,
p
dim.
p
Sehr ruhig.
Molto tranquillo.
-chen mahnt!
to wake!
dolce
f
Ha- -bet Acht!
Have a care!
mf
pp
f
Ha- -bet Acht
Have a care!
mf
p
più p

B.

Bald ent - weicht die be -
Day - - light comes! die be -

morendo

verhallend
morendo

Immer sehr ruhig.
Sempre molto tranquillo

B.

Nacht! _____
ware! _____

morendo

Red.

pp

I.

p Isolda.
Lausch',
List,

pp

I.
T.

Tristan.

Ge - lieb - ter! Lass mich ster - ben!
be - lov - ed! Let me die now!

cresc.

f dim.

p

I.

Isolda (gradually raising herself a little)

Neid' - - sche Wa - che!
En - - vious watcher!

f

Tristan (remaining reclining)

Isolda.

Nie er - wachen! Doch der Tag muss Tri - stan we - cken?
I'll not waken! Will the day not Tris - tan wak - en?

dim. *più p*

Tristan (raising his head a little)

Ein wenig belebend.
Poco animando.

Lass den Tag dem To - de wei - chen!
Let the day to Death be giv - en!

cresc. *dim.* *p*

Isolda (senz' impeto)

Tag und Tod mit glei - chen Strei - chen soll - ten uns -
Day and Death as one have striv - en, by them shall

p *p* *p*

Sehr ruhig.
Molto tranquillo. **Tristan** (raising himself slightly)

- re Lieb' er - rei - chen? Uns - re Lie - be? Tri -
- our love be riv - en? This our pas - sion? Tris -

p *cresc.* *p dolce*

18325

T.
-stan's Lie - be? Dein' und mein, — I-sol - de's Lie - be?
-tan's pas - sion? Thine and mine, — I-sol - da's pas - sion?
p
cresc.
Wel - ches To - des Strei - chen
How - so Death were giv - en,
f
p
cresc.
könn - te je — sie wei - chen? Stünd' er vor mir, der mächt'ge
it could ne'er be riv - en. Stood he by me, this might-y
f dim.
più f
pp
sehr ruhig
molto tranquillo
etwas zurückhaltend
poco ritenuto
Tod, wie er mir Leib und Le-ben be-droht, die ich so wil-lig der Lie-be
Death, men-ac-ing life and limb with his breath, that I would light-ly for love be
p
più p
poco ritenuto
a tempo
las - se, wie wä - re sei-nen Strei-chen die Lie - be selbst zu er-
leav-ing, e'en so, his death-stroke nev-er our love were a - ble to
a tempo
pp
cresc.
f

Died I for her I'd so gladly die for, how were it my love with me should
perish? The ev-er-liv-ing to die with-in me? Yet
died his pas-sion not in him, how then could Tris-tan die to
pas - - - sion?

Etwas zögernd und sehr ruhig.
Poco ritenuto e molto tranquillo.
(nestling with his head yet closer to Isolda)

rei-chen?
sev-er.
Stürb' ich nun ihr, der so gern ich
ster-be, wie könn-te die Lie-be mit mir
ster-ben, die e-wig le-ben-de mit mir en-den? Doch,

Langsam (wie zuvor).
Lento (come prima).
a tempo
stür-be nie sei-ne Lie-be, wie stür-be dann Tri-stan sei-ner

Etwas zögernd.
Poco rallent.
Lie - - - be?

175

18325

Etwas belebend, aber unmerklich.
Animando, ma molto poco.

sehr weich
dolcissimo

Doch___ uns-re___ Lie - be,
But___ this_our___ pas - sion___

p espress.

poco riten. *a tempo*

heisst sie nicht Tri - stan und I - sol - de?
call we not Tris - tan and I - sol - da's?

poco riten. *a tempo*

p *più p* *p ausdrucksvoll espressivo*

Dies sü - sse Wört-lein: und,___
That sweet - est word-let "and:"___

più p

was es bin - det, der Lie - be Bund,___ wenn___ Tri - stan
How it binds_us in lov - ing bonds!___ should___ Tris - tan

pp dolce *poco cresc.*

Sehr ruhig.
Molto tranquillo.

stürb,___ zer - stört' es nicht der Tod?
die,___ were that word loos'd by Death?

pp

con Ped.

18325

Tristan *(molto tranquillo)*

Was stür-be dem Tod, als was uns stört, was Tri-stan wehrt,___ I-
And what could Death kill, but trou-bles deep, that Tristan keep___ I-

sol - de im-mer zu lie - ben, e - wig ihr nur zu le -
sold' for ev - er from lov - ing, and_for her ev-er liv -

più p   *pp*

Isolda.

ben? Doch dieses Wört-lein: und,___ wär' es zerstört, wie
ing? Yet for this word-let "and:"___ were it de-stroyed, ex-

cresc.   *sf*

langsam
lento

an-ders als mit I-sol-de's eig'-nem Le - ben wär' Tri - stan der Tod ge-
cept from heart of I-sold' the life were driv - en, could Tris - tan to death be

p   *cresc.*   *ff dim.*

Nicht schleppend.
Con moto.   *(Tristan, with expressive gestures, draws Isolda gently to him)*   **Tristan**

ge - ben?   So
giv - en?   So

p dolce   *più p*   *pp*   *ppp*

18325

Die sechs ♪ genau den sechs ♪ des frühern 3/4 Takts entsprechend.
The six ♪ exactly equivalent to those of the 3/4 movement before.

I.
trennt, ohn' Er-wa-chen,
part, ne'er to wak-en,
T.
e-wig ei-nig, oh-ne End',
Aye u-nit-ed, ne'er to end,
immer
sempre
pp
I.
na-men-los in
name-less there by
T.
ohn' Er-ban-gen, in
peace un-bound-ed, by
poco cresc.
I.
Lieb' um-fan-gen, ganz uns selbst ge-ge-
love sur-round-ed, each to oth-er giv-
T.
Lieb' um-fan-gen, ganz uns ge-ge-
love sur-round-ed, each to oth-er giv-
pp
cresc.

I.
ben,   der   Lie - be nur _____ zu le - - -
ing,   for   love _____ a - lone _____ there liv - -

T.
ben,   der   Lie - be nur   zu le - -
ing,   for   love   a - lone   there liv- -

p   *dolce*   *dim.*   *più p*

(Isolda, as if overpowered, droops her head upon his breast)

I. - - ben! / - - ing!

Brangæna. *f*
B. Ha - bet Acht! _____ / Have a care! _____

T. - - ben! / - - ing!

pp   *un poco cresc.* —

B. Ha - bet Acht! _____ Schon / Have a care! _____ Night

dim.

verhallend / *morendo*

B.
weicht dem Tag _____ die Nacht! / yields to day! _____ be - ware! _____

morendo   *morendo*

Tristan (bends smilingly down to Isolda)
(Isolda gazes fondly up at Tristan)
T.
Soll ich lau - - - schen?
Shall I lis - - - ten?
pp
Isolda.
riten.
a tempo
I.
Lass mich ster - ben!
Let me die so!
riten.
a tempo
f dim.
p
Tristan (more gravely)
Isolda (more affected)
riten.
T.
I.
Muss ich wa - - chen?
Must I wak - - en?
Nie er - wa-chen!
I'll not wak - en!
riten.
f
dim.
p
Tristan (stringendo)
a tempo
T.
Soll der Tag noch Tri - stan we - cken?
Must the day yet Tris - tan wak - en?
a tempo
etwas drängender
un poco più stringendo
p
cresc.

Isolda (with enthusiasm)   *molto riten.*   **Immer mehr belebend.**
Sempre più animando.

Tristan.

Lass den Tag dem— To-de wei-chen!
Let the day to— death be giv-en!

Des
May

molto riten.

f sehr ausdrucksvoll
molto espressivo

p

cresc.

Isolda (with ris-

Ta - ges Dräu-en nun trotz - ten wir so? Sei - nem
day - light's men-ace so light - ly be met? From its

f 3   3   3

3

Immer belebter.
Sempre più mosso.

ing ecstasy)

3

Trug— e - wig zu flieh'n!
lies— could we but fly!

f   *dim.*   *p*   *cresc.*

Tristan.

Sein däm - mern-der Schein— ver - scheuch - te uns
Then glim - mer-ing morn— would fright— us no

Lebhaft, mit Steigerung
Allegro, con elevazione.
Isolda (with ecstatic gesture, rising to her feet)
(Tristan follows her;
I.
E - - wig währ' uns die Nacht!
Nay, if night were for aye!
T.
nie?
more?
f
p
cresc.
fp
they embrace in a fond ecstasy)
fp
fp
fp
fp molto cresc.
O
O
rallent.
più f
Sehr lebhaft und schnell.
Molto vivo e presto.
ew' - - ge Nacht, sü - -
end - - less night, bless - -
ew' - - ge Nacht, sü - -
end - - less night, bless - -
ff
dim.
p dolce

I. -sse Nacht! Hehr er-
-ed night! Love's sub-

T. -sse Nacht! Hehr er-
-ed night! Love's sub-

p *molto cresc.* *ff*

I. hab' - - ne Lie - - bes-
lim - - est, awe - - some

T. hab' - - ne Lie - - bes-
lim - - est, awe - - some

dim.

p dolce

I. nacht! Wen du um-fan - gen, wie
night! Him that thou smil - ing could

T. nacht! wem du ge - lacht,
night! tak'st to thy breast,

p *più p* *pp*

I.
wär' oh-ne Ban- -gen aus dir er je_ er-
he un-re- vil- -ing be wak-ened from thy_
T.
wie wär' oh-ne Ban-gen er aus dir er-
could he un-re-vil-ing wak-en from thy
p
cresc.
wacht? Nun ban-ne das Ban-gen,
rest? Now ban-ish fore-bod-ings,
dim.
wacht? Nun ban- -ne das
rest? Now ban- -ish fore-
f
dim.
p
hol- -der Tod,_ seh- -nend ver-
kind- -ly Death,_ hoped- -for and
Ban- -gen, seh- -nend ver-
bod- -ings, hoped- -for and
cresc.
ff

Voice I: lang - ter Lie - bes - tod! _____ In dei - nen
longed - for love in Death! _____ Thine arms are

Tenor: lang - ter Lie - bes - tod! _____
longed - for love in Death! _____

Voice I: Ar - men, dir ge - weiht, _____
round us, thine are we, _____

Tenor: In dei - nen Ar - men, dir ge -
Thine arms are round us, thine are

Voice I: ur - hei - lig Er - war - men, von Er -
warm slum - ber has bound _____ us, from all

Tenor: weiht, _____ ur - hei - lig Er -
we, _____ warm slum - ber has

I.
wa- -chens Noth be- freit!
fear of wak- -ing free!
T.
war- men, von Er- wa- chens Noth be- freit!
bound us, from all fear of wak- ing free!
molto cresc.
ff
f dim.
p
Wie es fas- sen, wie es las- sen,
How to use it, how to lose it,
p espress.
Fern der
Sun to
f
die- -se Won- -ne, fern der
from this Won- -der, sun to
cresc.

I.
Son- - ne, fern der Ta- - ge
sun- - der, far the mor- - row's
T.
Son- - ne, fern der Ta- - -
sun- - der, far the mor- - -
I.
p
Trenn-nungs-kla - ge! Oh - ne Wäh - nen,
part-ing sor - rows! Truth dis - cern - ing,
T.
- ge Tren- - nungs-kla - ge!
- row's part- - ing sor - rows!
f
dim.
I.
zart
dolce
oh - ne Ban - gen
fear dis - pel - ling,
T.
sanf- - tes Seh - nen;
Sweet our yearn - ing;
dolce
p
p

I.
T.
p
dolce
süss Ver- lan- -gen; oh - ne
hope fore - tell- -ing; pain ef- -
We- -hen hehr Ver- ge - hen;
fac- -ing, death em - brac - ing;
hehr Ver- ge - hen;
death em - brac - ing;
oh - ne Schmach - ten hold Um -
love - be- -hold- -en, night- - -en -
hold Um -
night- - -en -

I.
T.
nach- -ten;
fold- -en;
nach ten; oh- -ne Mei- -den,
fold -en; near for ev- -er,
cresc.
p
oh- -ne Schei-
Ne'er to sev-
oh- -ne Schei- -den, traut
ne'er to sev- -er, none
molto cresc.
f
-den, traut al- -lein,
-er, none to come,
al- -lein,
to come,
più f
pp

I.
T.
e - wig heim, in un - ge - mess' - nen
here our home, in re - gions past all
e - wig heim, in un - ge - mess' - nen
here our home, in re - gions past all
poco cresc.
p
Räu - men ü - - - ber - sel' - ges -
mea - sure, dreams of bliss - ful
Räu - men ü - - - ber -
mea - sure, dreams of
dim.
più p
pp
Ped.
Träu - men: Du - I - sol - de,
plea - sure: Thou I - sol - da,
zart
dolce
sel' - ges Träu - men: Tri - - - stan
bliss - ful plea - sure: Tris - - - tan
dolce
Ped.

I. Tri - - - - - stan ____ ich, ____
Tris - - - - - tan ____ I, ____

T. du, ____ ich ____
thou, ____ I ____

p dolce

Red. ✲ Red. ✲ Red. ✲

I. nicht ____ mehr I -
no ____ more I -

T. ____ I - sol - de,
____ I - sol - da,

più p

Red. ✲ Red. ✲ Red. ✲

I. sol - - de!
sol - - da!

T. nicht ____ mehr ____ Tri - - stan!
no ____ more ____ Tris - - tan!

pp *morendo*

Red. ✲ Red. ✲ Red. ✲

Sehr drängend.
Molto affrettando.

I. Oh - -ne Nen - nen, oh - -ne Tren - nen,

Name - -less ev - er, part - -ed nev - er,

T. E - - - - - wig!

End - - - - - less!

p molto cresc.

I. neu Er - ken - nen, neu Ent - bren - nen,

new - -ly know - ing, fresh - -ly glow - ing,

T. End - - - - - los! End -

End - - - - - less! End -

I. end - los e - - - - - - - - - -

end - less ev - - - - - - - - - -

- - - - -los e - -wig ein be -

- - - - -less ev - -er all in

f *più f* *ff* *sehr gehalten, molto tenuto*

Immer etwas drängend.
Sempre poco stringendo.

I. - -wig ein be - wusst: end - - -los

- -er all in all: end - - -less

T. wusst, e - - wig ein be - wusst:

all: end - - less all in all:

aber nicht gebunden
ma non legato *ff*

immer
sempre f

18325

I.
T.
e - wig
ev - er,
heiss er -
pas - sion
e - wig
ev - er
end - los
end - less,
glüh - ter Brust,
ne'er to pall,
höch - ste
love's su -
Lie - bes - lust!
prem - est thrall!
end - los
end - less
e - wig
ev - er,
Heiss er - glüh - ter
Pas - sion ne'er to
mp
più f

Noch drängender.
Più stringendo.
I.
höch - - - - ste Lie - - - -
love's su - prem - - -
T.
Brust höch - ste Lie - - - bes-
pall, love's su - prem - - - est
gebunden
legato
cresc.
p
I.
- - bes - lust! Höch - - - -
- - est thrall! Love's
T.
lust! Höch - ste Lie - bes - lust!
thrall! Love's su - prem - est thrall!
nicht gebunden
non legato
molto cresc.
I.
- - - - ste Lie - - bes -
su - prem - - est
T.
Höch - - ste Lie - - - bes -
Love's su - prem - - - est
più f

Scene III.

Sehr schnell (♩ merklich schneller als zuvor).
Prestissimo (♩ perceptibly quicker than before).

Isolda.

lust!
thrall!

Brangæna (utters a piercing shriek)

(Schrei)
(Shriek)

Tristan (Tristan and Isolda keep their positions as if entranced)

lust!
thrall!

Kurvenal (rushing in with drawn sword)

Ret - te dich,
Save thy-self,

ff

fp molto cresc.

(He looks off stage behind him in great alarm)

Tristan!
Tristan!

(Mark, Melot and courtiers, in hunting-dress, come quickly from the avenue towards the front, and pause

Wieder das vorhergehende Hauptzeitmass (♩ mässiger).
The previous tempo (♩ slower).
Sehr lebhaft. Molto vivace.

ff

sempre stacc.

in amazement before the lovers. In the meantime Brangæna descends from the turret, and rushes towards

ff

Isolda, who, with instinctive shame, leans with averted face upon the flowery bank. Tristan, with an e-

qually instinctive movement, with one arm spreads his cloak so as to conceal Isolda from the eyes of the

newcomers._ In this position he remains for some time, his eyes steadily fixed upon the men who look at

him with varied emotions._ Morning dawns)

Allmählich etwas langsamer.
Poco a poco allargando.

Mässig bewegt.
Con moto moderato.

Tristan.

Melot (to Mark)

Der ö - de Tag_ zum letz - ten Mal!
The day has dawned_ and 'tis the last!
Das_
Now,_

_ sollst du, Herr, mir sa - gen, ob_ ich ihn recht ver-klagt? Das dir zum
_ good my lord, I ask you, have_ I ac-cused him right? I said I'd

Pfand ich gab, ob ich mein Haupt ge-wahrt? Ich zeigt' ihn dir in off'-ner
stake my head,_ well, have I saved it now? Thou'st seen him in the fla-grant

sf p poco cresc.

That. Namen und Ehr' hab' ich ge-treu vor Schan - de dir be-
act! Honour and fame, thanks to my faith, I've shield - ed thee from

f

Mässig langsam.
Lento moderato.

Mark (violently affected, then with trembling voice)

wahrt.
shame.

sehr ausdrucksvoll

Tha - test du's wirklich? Wähnst du das?_
Hast thou tho', tru - ly? Think'st thou so?

molto espressivo

dim.

p

p

f

p

18325

sehr getragen
con molto portamento

Sieh' ihn dort, den
See him there, the

Treu'sten al-ler Treu-en; blick' auf ihn,— den freundlichsten der
tru-est of the trust-ed. look on him,— whose friend-ship was the

Freunde: sei-ner Treu-e frei'-ste That traf mein
firm-est! Yet his friendliest deed to me smote my

Herz mit feindlichstem Ver-rath!
heart with deadliest treacher-y!

Trog mich Tristan, sollt' ich hof-fen, was sein Trü-gen mir ge-
Trick'd by Tristan! Shall I flat-ter what his treach-er-y could

18325

etwas zurückhaltend / poco riten. — Lebhaft. Vivace.

trof-fen, sei durch Me-lots Rath red-lich mir be-wahrt?
shat-ter should by Me-lot be real-ly saved for me?

Tristan (with convulsive violence) — *accel.*

Tags - ge-spen - ster! Mor-gen-träu-me! täuschend und
Ghosts of Day-light! Dreams of morn-ing! trick-y and

rallent. — **Mark** (with deep emotion)

wüst! Entschwebt! Ent-weicht! Mir dies?
void! A-vaunt! a-way! Thou, too?

Wieder mässig langsam. — Lento moderato, come prima. — Sehr zurückhaltend. molto riten.
Etwas bewegter, doch streng im Zeitmass. — Poco animato, ma in tempo. (Bewegter)(more agitated)

Dies, Tri-stan, mir?— Wo-hin nun Treu-e, da Tri-stan mich be-
Tris-tan, to me?— Where truth it-self, then, if Tris-tan prove un-

trog? Wo-hin nun Ehr' und ech-te Art, da al-ler Eh-ren Hort,— da Tri-
true? Where now good faith and deal-ing fair, since honour's soul it-self,— since Tris-

riten.

M.: - stan sie ver - lor? Die Tri - stan sich zum Schild er-kor, wo-hin ist
- tan's lost them all? The vir - tue Tris-tan took for shield, where is that

riten. *ten.* *cresc.*

Breit. Largamente. *rallent.* *(langsam) (lento)*

M.: Tu-gend nun ent-floh'n, da mei-nen Freund sie flieht, da Tri - stan mich ver-
vir-tue van - ish'd now, that from him fell a - way, and Tris - tan can be-

rallent. dim.

Wieder mässig langsam.
Lento moderato, come prima.

M.: (Tristan slowly drops his eyes to the ground; his face expresses his increasing sorrow as Mark continues)

rieth?
tray?

ausdrucksvoll und weich
espressivo e dolce

Belebend.
Animando.

M.: Wo - zu die Dienste oh - ne Zahl, der Eh - ren
What was thy ser-vice all un-told, that hon - our,

M.: Ruhm, der Grö-sse Macht, die Mar - - ken du ge-wannst; musst' Ehr' und
fame and pow'r of place thou won'st ___ for Mark, the King? Must hon - our,

poco cresc. *cresc. -*

Mehr belebend.
Più animando.

Ruhm, Gröss' und Macht, muss-te die Dien-ste oh-ne Zahl dir Mar -
fame, power and place, must all thy ser-vic-es un - told, by Marks

- ke's Schmach be - zah-len?   Dünk - te zu
- dis-grace be paid for?   Thought ye so

we - nig dich sein Dank, dass, was du ihm er - wor-ben, Ruhm und
lit - tle worth his thanks, that all that you had won him, fame and

Reich, er zu Erb' und Ei - - gen dir gab?
for - tune, he made you heir - to it all?

Da kin-der-los einst schwand sein Weib, so liebt' er
When child-less his wife he had lost, so loved he

dich, dass nie auf's Neu' sich Mar - ke wollt' ver - mäh-len.
thee, that ne'er a - new could Mark e'er wish to mar-ry.

Belebt. Con moto.

Da al-lesVolk zu Hof und Land mit Bitt'__ und Dräu - en in ihn drang, die
When all the country, all the court with pray'rs and threats a-round him throng'd, a

Kö - ni-gin dem Lan-de, die Gat-tin sich zu kie-sen; da sel - ber
queen to give the country, him-self a wife to take him, when thou thy-

du den Ohm beschworst, des Ho - fes Wunsch, des Lan - des Wil - len güt-
self didst ev - er urge that what the court and coun - try want-ed, gra-

- lich zu er-fül-len: in Wehr wi - der Hof und Land, inWehr selbst ge-gen
- cious-ly be granted: ar - rayed 'gainst the court and folk, array'd a - gainst thy-

18325

M.

dich, mit List und Gü - te wei-gerte er sich, bis, Tristan, du ihm
self, with skill and kind-ness did he not de - cline, till, Tristan, thou didst

p *f* *p* ten.

Belebend.
Animando.

M.

drohtest, für immer zu mei-den Hof und Land, wür-dest du sel - ber
threaten, for ev - er to go from court and land, didst thou the mis - sion

mf *f* *p* cresc. -

zurückhaltend
rallent.

M.

nicht ent-sandt, dem Kö - nig die Braut zu frein. Da liess ers denn so
not receive, a bride for the king to woo, and so he let thee

f *p* *zurückhaltend*
rall.

Viel langsamer. *sehr zart*
Molto più lento. *dolcissimo*

M.

sein. - Diess wunder-vol - le Weib,
go. - This wondrous fair, a wife

p *zart* *p* *zart*
dolce *espress.*

M.

das mir dein Muth ge-wann, wer durft' es se - hen, wer es
thy might for me did win; who could have seen her, who have

sehr zart
dolciss. *p*

18325

ken-nen, wer mit Stol - ze sein es nen-nen, oh - ne se - lig sich zu
known her, who with pride as wife could own her, nor es-teem himself most

p · *poco cresc.* · *più cresc.* · *f*

prei - sen? Der mein Wil-le nie zu na - hen wag-te, der mein
hap - py? My free will had nev-er dared to take her, mine my

p

Wunsch ehrfurchtscheu ent-sag-te, die so herr-lich hold er-ha-ben mir die
wish me for-bade to make her, she, so gracious, good, who on - ly could have

più p · *p dolce* · *poco cresc.*

See - le muss-te la - ben, trotz Feind und Ge-fahr, die fürst-liche Braut
cheered my life so lone - ly, spite dan-ger and foe, this queenliest bride,

f f f

Wieder bewegter.
Più animato.

brachtest du mir dar.
her didst thou be - stow.

f dim. f p

206

Nun, da durch sol-chen Be-sitz mein Herz du fühl-sa-mer
When, by thy gift, had my heart the more grown soft-er for

schufst als sonst dem Schmerz, dort wo am weich-sten, zart und
pain than e'er be-fore, hast thou a-gainst it, un-pro-

of-fen, würd' ich ge-trof-fen, nie zu hof-fen, dass je ich könn-te ge-
tect-ed, thy blow di-rect-ed! Hope is o-ver, that e'er a-gain I re-

sun-den: warum so sehrend, Un-se-li-ger, dort nun mich ver-
cov-er. O why so deep-ly, most wretch-ed man, here, this wise, didst

wun-den? Dort mit der Waf-fe quä-len-dem Gift, das Sinn und
wound me? Thus with a poi-son'd weapon to pierce, that brain and

18325

M.
Hirn mir sen-gend ver - sehrt, das mir dem Freund die Treu - e ver-
soul doth rav-age and rend, that turneth false my faith - ful-lest
p
cresc.
f
poco accel.
wehrt, mein off' - nes Herz er-füllt mit Ver-dacht, dass ich nun
friend; my o - pen heart to fill with mis-trust, that spy a-
p
f
poco accel.
pp
rall.
heimlich in dunk-ler Nacht den Freund lau-schend be - schlei -
bout in the night I must, and watch him I be - friend -
rall.
poco cresc.
dim.
pp
che, mei-ner Eh - ren En-de er-rei - che?
ed, and to find my hon-our was end - ed?
molto cresc.
ff
p molto cresc.
Die kein Him -
If no heav'n
ff

riten.   a tempo

M.

- mel er-löst, war-um mir die-se Höl-le?
I may win, why this hell do I suf-fer?

riten. a tempo

ff   ff   dim. -

rall.   *molto rall.*

M.

Die kein E - - - lend sühnt, war-why
If no ills it soothe, why

rall.   *molto rall.*

p

Sehr langsam.
Molto adagio.   *a tempo*   sehr
molto

M.

um mir die - se Schmach? Den
falls the pain on me? Whence

a tempo

sehr ausdrucksvoll
molto espressivo   *(weich)*
(dolce)   pp

langsam.
adagio.

M.

un-er-forsch - lich tief ge - heimniss-vol-len Grund, wer macht der Welt ihn
un-dis-cov - er'd, deep, mys - te - rious causes flow, who e'er the world shall

p   più p   pp

Langsam.
Adagio.

Tristan (raising his eyes sympathizingly to Mark)

M.
T.

kund? O Kö-nig, das kann ich dir nicht
show? O monarch! That can I nev - er

p   p   più p   pp

T.
sa - gen; und was du frägst, das kannst du nie er-
tell thee; what thou dost ask, it nev - er shall be
p
pp
(He turns towards Isolda, who looks up longingly at him)
fah-ren.
an-swer'd.
p
espress.
sf
p
p
p
Mässig langsam. (♩ langsamer als zuvor ♪)
Lento moderato. (The ♩ slower than the previous ♪)
rallent.
ruhig tranquillo
mf
più p
morendo
p
Tristan.
Wo - hin nun Tri - stan schei - det, willst du, I -
Where Tris - tan now de - part - eth, wilt thou, I -
mf
dim.
più p
pp
sold', ihm fol - gen? Dem Land, das Tri - stan
sol - da, fol - low? The land I have in
pp
più p
pp

poco riten.   *a tempo*

T.

meint, der Son-ne Licht nicht scheint: es ist das dun - kel - mächt' - ge
mind, the sun-light doth not find; it is the dark - some land of

pp *poco riten.*   *a tempo*

T.

Land, da - raus die Mut - ter mich ent-sandt, als, den im To - de sie em-
night, where me my moth - er brought to light, and as in death she did con-

dolce

T.

pfan - gen, im Tod sie liess an das Licht _____ ge - lan - gen.
ceive me, in death to lan-guish in light _____ did leave me.

più **p**

T.

Was, da sie mich ge - bar, ihr Lie - bes - ber - ge
What did shield her from earth, what time she gave me

p

p *dolce*

poco riten.

T.

war, das Wun - der - reich der Nacht, aus der ich einst er -
birth, the deep and won - drous night, that once I left for

poco riten.

T. wacht: das bie-tet dir Tri-stan, da-hin geht er vor-an; ob sie ihm
light, that Tris-tan of-fers thee, and thith-er first goes he. If she in

a tempo
p dolce

T. fol-ge treu und hold, das sag' ihm nun I-sold'!
love and faith will go, I-sold' shall let him know!

f *p* *più p* *pp*

Etwas bewegt.
Isolda. Con moto.

I. Als für ein frem-des Land der Freund sie ein-stens
When her to for-eign lands as friend thou once didst

p *p*

zurückhaltend
ritenuto *rall.* *a tempo*

I. warb, dem Un-hol-den treu und hold musst' I-sol-de fol-gen.
woo, the un-faith-ful full of faith did I-sol-da fol-low.

langsamer *poco riten.* *a tempo*
p *più lento* *più p* *pp* *p*

I. Nun führst du in dein Ei-gen, dein Er-be mir zu zei-gen;
To realms of thine now go-ing, thine her-i-tage art show-ing:

più p *pp*

18325

riten.

wie flöh' ich wohl das Land, das al - le Welt um-spannt? Wo
Why should I fear that space, that doth the world em - brace? To

pp   *riten.*
più p

a tempo

Tri-stan's Haus und Heim, da kehr' I - sol - - de ein: auf dem sie
Tris-tan's house and home, there will I - sol - - da come: the course she

a tempo
dolce   *cresc.*

rallent.   *molto rit.*

fol - ge treu und hold, den Weg hun zeig I -
true and fair must hold, that course now show I -

f   *p*   *più p*   *pp*   *molto rit.*

Langsam und zögernd. (Tristan bends slowly down to her and kisses her gently on her forehead)
Lento e ritardando.

sold'!
sold'!

pp sehr zart
dolciss.

(Melot starts angrily forward)

morendo

Lebhaftes Zeitmass.
Tempo vivo.

Melot (drawing his sword)

Ver-räther! Ha! Zur Ra - che, Kö-nig! Dul - dest du die-se Schmach?
Thou traitor! Ha! A-venge thee, monarch! Canst thou bear this affront?

Tristan (draws his sword and turns quickly round)

Wer wagt sein Le - ben an das mei - ne?
Who's he will risk his life a - gainst me?

(Fixing his gaze on Melot)

Mein Freund war
My friend was

etwas zurückhaltend
poco ritenuto   *accel.*

der, er minn-te mich hoch und theu - er; um
he, and tru - ly and well he loved me; my

etwas zurückhaltend
poco riten.

a tempo

Ehr' und Ruhm mir war er be-sorgt wie
name and fame were dear-er to him than

18325

accel.

T. Kei-ner. Zum Ü-ber-muth trieb er mein
an-y. He drove my heart to be too

Noch lebhafter.
Più vivo.

T. Herz; die Schar führt'er, die mich ge-drängt,
bold, 'twas he led those that urged me on

Sehr lebhaft.
Molto vivace.   *molto riten.*

T. Ehr' und Ruhm mir zu meh - ren, dem Kö - nig dich zu ver-
fame and name to ex-tend me by wed-ding thee to the

Etwas langsamer.
Poco meno mosso.

T. mäh - - len! Dein Blick, I - sol - de,
King there! Thine eyes, I - sol - da,

accel.   *riten.*

T. blen-det'auch ihn, aus Ei-fer ver-rieth mich der Freund ___ dem
blind-ed him, too, and jealous, be-trayed me my friend ___ to the

accel.

18325

Wieder lebhaft.
Vivace, come prima.

Kö - nig, den ich ver-rieth!_
mon - arch whom I betrayed!_

(He sets on Melot)

Wehr' dich! Melot!
Guard thee! Melot!

(As Melot thrusts his sword at him, Tristan lets his fall and sinks wounded into Kurvenal's arms; Isolda throws herself upon his breast. Mark holds back Melot. The Curtain falls quickly)

Act III.

Mässig langsam.
Lento moderato.
f
dim.
p
gedehnt
steso
più p
pp
gedehnt
steso
p ausdrucksvoll
espressivo
poco cresc.
(sehr lang)
(molto lunga)
f dim. più p
p
cresc.
f
dim.
p
gedehnt
steso
più p
pp
weich und ausdrucksvoll
dolce ed espressivo
dim.
pp
p
cresc.
più cresc.
più f
ff
f dim.
p
più p
(The Curtain rises.)
pp

Scene I.

(The garden of a castle. At one side are high turrets, on the other a low breastwork broken by a watch-tower; at back the castle-gate. The situation is supposed to be on rocky cliffs; through openings one looks over a wide sea to the horizon. The whole scene gives an impression of being **ownerless, badly kept,** here and there delapidated and overgrown.

In the foreground inside lies Tristan sleeping on a couch, under the shade of a great lime-tree, extended as if lifeless. At his head sits Kurvenal, bending over him in grief, and anxiously listening to his breath - ing. From without comes the sound of a Shepherd's pipe)

(The Shepherd shows the upper half of his body over the breastwork, and looks in sympatheti-cally)

a tempo

(Orchestra.)

Shepherd.

(Kurvenal turns his head a little towards him)

Kurwe-nal! He!   Sag', Kurwe-nal!   Hör' doch, Freund! Wacht er noch nicht?
Kur-ve-nal! Ho!   Say, Kur-ve-nal!   Hear, my friend! Has he not waked?

Kurvenal. (He shakes his head sadly)

Erwachte er,   wär's doch nur, um für im-mer zu ver-
And if he woke,   it would be but to part from us for

schei - - den: er-schien zu-
ev - - er: un-less that

vor die Ärz-tin nicht, die einz' - - ge, die uns hilft.
doc-tress come, for she a-lone ___ can help us now.

Shepherd.

Sah'st du noch nichts? kein Schiff noch auf der See? Ei-ne and're
See'st nothing yet? no ship yet on the sea? Oh! a dif-f'rent

Wei - se hör - test du dann, so lustig als ich sie nur kann.
tune then pipe_ you I would, as mer-ry as ev-er I could.

Nun sag' auch ehr - lich, alter Freund: was hat's mit un-serm Herrn?
But tell me tru - ly, good my friend: what is it ails our lord?

Kurvenal.

Lass die Fra - ge: du kannst's doch nie er - fah-ren. Eif - rig
Leave the ques-tion: thou ne'er may'st know the an-swer. Watch ye

späh', und siehst du ein Schiff, so spie-le lu-stig und hell!
well; and sight ye a sail, pipe up then lust-y and loud!

(The Shepherd turns round and scans the sea, shading his eyes with his hand) Shepherd.

Oed' und
Bare and

a tempo

sehr gedehnt
molto stesso

più p

pp

f dim.

leer   das Meer!
clear   the sea!

(He puts the reed-pipe to his mouth and withdraws, playing)

(Cor anglais on the stage.)

p

cresc.

sf

pp

pp

ritard.

3   3   3   accel.

p   sf

dim.

Langsam.
Lento.

sehr zögernd
molto allarg.

p

allmählich schwindend
poco a poco morendo

pp

Tristan (without moving, faintly)   (He opens his eyes and turns his head a little)

Die al-te Wei - se;   was weckt sie mich?   Wo bin ich?
Ah! 'tis the old   tune;   why wakes it me?   Where am I?

Kurvenal.   (Kurvenal starts in surprise)   p

Ha!
Ha!

a tempo

3   3

pp

poco cresc.

3

Lebhaft.
Vivace.
Kurvenal.
Ha! Die-se Stimme! Sei - ne Stim - - - - - me!
Ha! He is speaking! yes, I heard him!
p cresc.
sf
f
Tri - stan! Her - re! Mein Held!
Tris - tan! Mas - ter! my lord!
fp
Mein Tri - - - - - - - - stan!
My Tris - - - - - - - - tan!
p cresc.
Tristan (with effort)
Wer ruft mich?
Who calls me?
Kurvenal.
End - lich!
Life! at
End - lich! Le - - - - ben, o Le - - - - - ben!
last! He liv - - - - eth, he liv - - - - - eth!
dim.

K. Sü — — — sses Le — ben meinem Tri-stan neu ge-
Life, dear life is to my Tris-tan once more

rallent.

Etwas langsam.
Poco lento.
Tristan (feebly).

K. ge — ben! Kurwenal— du? Wo war ich? Wo bin ich?
T. giv — en! Kur-ve-nal! thou? Where was I? Where am I?

più p   *più p*   *pp*

Vorheriges Zeitmass.
L'istesso tempo
($\textstyle\frac{1}{2} = \frac{1}{2}$)

Kurvenal.

K. Wo du bist? In Frie — den,
Where thou art? In safe — ty,

nicht kurz gestossen
non troppo staccato

($\textstyle\frac{1}{2} = \frac{1}{2}$)   *p*   *cresc. —*

K. si-cher und frei! Ka — re-ol, Herr:
peace-ful and free! Ka — re-ol, Sire:

p   *cresc. —*

Tristan.   Kurvenal.

K. kennst du die Burg der Vä — — ter nicht? "Mei - ner Väter? Sieh' dich nur
T. dost thou not know thy fa — — thers' towers? How? my fathers'? Look thee a-
K.

f   *p*   *più p*   *sf*

18325

Belebend.
Animando.

Tristan.

Kurvenal.

K. T. K.

um!   Was erklang mir?   Des Hir-ten Wei - se
round!   Heard I mu-sic?   The shepherd's pipe thou

dim.   *p*   *più p*   *p*

K.

hör - test du wie - der; am   Hü-gel ab hü-tet er dei-ne Her-
heard - est a - play-ing; from   yon-der hill, where he thy flocks is feed-

cresc.   *f*   *p*   *f*

Tristan.

Kurvenal

K. T. K.

- de.   Mei - ne Her-de?   Herr,   das mein'ich!
- ing.   Mine the flocks, too?   Sire,   I say so!

dim.   *p*   *più p*   *cresc.*

Belebend.
Animando.

K.

Dein das Haus,   Hof____ und Burg!   Das Volk,   ge-still
Thine this Hall,   court____ and tower!   The folk   still

fp   *cresc.*

K.

treu dem trau - ten Herrn,   so gut es konnt',   hat's
true to trust - ed Lord,   as best they might,   have

f   *fp*   3   *cresc.*   3

K. Haus und Hof ge-pflegt, das einst mein Held zu Erb'und
kept the house and hall that once my lord to have and

K. Ei-gen an Leut' und Volk verschenkt, als Al-les er verliess, in frem-de Land' zu
hold to thy serfs and vas-sals gave, when all he left be-hind, to for-eign lands to

Tristan. *Kurvenal.*

K.T. zieh'n. In wel-ches Land? Hei! Nach
T.K. fare. What for-eign land? Aye! To

Ein wenig breiter.
Poco più largamente.

K. Kornwall: kühn und won-nig, was sich da Glan-zes, Glückes und
Cornwall: where brave and happy, so much good for-tune, glo-ry and

poco rall.

K. Eh - - ren Tri - stan, mein Held, hehr er-trotzt!
hon - - our Tris - tan, my lord, no-bly won!

poco rall.

Etwas langsamer.
Poco più lento.

Tristan.
Bin ich in Kornwall?
Am I in Cornwall?

Kurvenal.
Nicht doch: in Ka - reol!
Ah! no! in Ka - reol!

gedehnt
steso

Tristan.
Wie kam ich
How came I

Etwas bewegter.
Poco più mosso.

Kurvenal.
her? Hei nun! Wie du kamst? Zu Ross rit-test du nicht; ein Schifflein führ-te dich
here? Eh now! How thou cam'st? A - horse camest thou not; a ship 'twas, car-ried thee

her: doch zu dem Schifflein hier auf den Schultern trug ich dich;
here: but to the ship, sire, 'twas on my shoulders bore I thee;

Etwas zurückhaltend.
Poco ritenuto.

Immer mehr belebend.
Sempre stringendo.

die sind breit: sie tru-gen dich dort zum Strand.
they are broad: they car-ried thee to the strand.

Nun_____ bist_____
Now_____ art_____

18325

K.
du da - heim, da - heim
thou at home, at home
cresc.
zu Land: im
on land; thy
Etwas breiter.
Poco largamente.
ech - ten Land, im Hei - mathland; auf eig' - ner Weid' und
pro - per land, thy na - tive land; thine own are mead and
f
immer
sempre f
Won - ne, im Schein der al - ten Son - - ne, dar -
mead - ow, in sun - shine and in shad - - ow; when
Etwas zurückhaltend.
Poco ritenuto.
in von Tod und Wun - den du se - - lig sollst ge - sun - - -
death and wounds are o - ver, where blithe - ly thou'lt re - cov - - -
f
dim.

Sehr allmählich ein wenig zurückhaltend.
Rallentando, ma poco a poco.

(He clings to Tristan's breast.)

K. den!
er.

zart
p dolce

più p

ausdrucksvoll
espressivo

dim.

Mässig langsam.
Lento moderato.

Tristan.

Dünkt dich das? Ich weiss es anders, doch kann ich's dir nicht sa-gen.
Think'st thou so? But I know bet-ter, and yet I can-not tell thee.

pp

pp

Wo ich er-wacht_ weilt' ich nicht; doch wo ich
Where I a-woke_ stayed I not; but where I

weil-te, das kann ich dir nicht sa-gen. Die Son - ne sah ich
tar-ried, yet that I can-not tell thee. The sun___ I did not

T. nicht, noch sah ich Land und Leute: doch, was ich sah, das kann ich dir nicht
see, nor yet the land or people: but, what I saw, nay, that I can not

più p · *pp* · *ppp*

T. sa-gen. Ich war, wo ich von je ge-we-sen, wo-hin auf je ich
tell thee. I was where I have been from ev-er, where I for ev-er

pp

T. geh': im wei-ten Reich der Wel-ten-nacht. Nur ein Wis-send ort uns ei-gen:
go: the bound-less realm of worldwide night. One thought on-ly there was left me:

pp

Sehr langsam. Adagio.
riten.

T. gött-lich ew'-ges Ur-ver-ges-sen! Wie schwand mir sei-ne
ev-er-last-ing out from think-ing! Why art thou lost past

ppp riten.

Sehr allmählich belebend.
Poco a poco più mosso.

T. Ah-nung? Sehn-süch-t'-ge Mahnung, nenn' ich dich, die neu dem
find-ing? Hate-ful re-minding, call I all, that back to

pp

Licht des Tag's mich zu - ge - trie - - ben? Was
light of day my spir - it driv - - eth, of

ein - zig mir ge - blie - ben, ein heiss
all I had de - priv - eth, a love

in - brün - stig Lie - ben, aus To - des Won - ne Grau - en jagt's mich das
that all sur - viv - eth, for death's most bless - ed twi - light I'm forc'd to

Licht zu schau - en, das trü - - gend hell und gol - den noch
face the day - light, that false - - ly bright and gold - en, still of

dir, I - - sol - - - - den,
thee, I - - sol - - - - da,

18325

Belebt (doch nicht schnell).
Animato (ma non allegro).

scheint! / shines!

I - sol - - - de noch im Reich der
I - sol - - - da still in realms of

Son - - - ne! / sun - - - light!

Im Ta - ges-schimmer noch I -
In day - light bright-ness still I-

sol - - de! / sol - - da!

Wel - ches
Ah, those

Seh - - - nen! / yearn - - - ings!

Wel - ches Ban - - - gen!
How I dread them!

Immer mehr belebend (auch im Zeitmass).
Sempre più animando (l'espressione come il tempo).

Sie_____ zu se - - hen, welch'_____ Ver-lan - gen!
Now_____ to see her I_____ am long - ing!

18325

T. Kra — chend hört' ich hin — ter mir schon des To-des Thor sich
I, that heard behind me crash of the door of death in

schliessen: weit nun steht es wie-der of-fen, der Son — ne
clos — ing! Wide it stands now once more o-pen; the stream — ing

Strah — len sprengt' es auf; mit hell er-schloss'nen Au — gen
sun — light burst it wide; with eyes by bril-liance blind — ed,

Bewegt. Con moto.

muss ich der Nacht ent-tau — — — chen, sie zu
must I the night re-lin — — — quish, for to

su — chen, sie zu se-hen; sie zu fin — den, in der
seek her, whom I cher-ish, and to greet her, and in

rallent.

ein - zig zu ver - ge - hen, zu ent - schwin - - den Tri -
her a - lone to per - ish: when I meet_____ her, Tris -

f *dim.* *rallent.* *più p*

Etwas gedehnt. Poco steso.

- stan ist ver - gönnt. Weh,_____ nun
- tan, I am doomed. Ah!_____ it

p *sf* *p* *sf*

wächst,_____ bleich und bang, mir des
breaks!_____ Dark and drear doth the

p *sf* *più f* *p* *sf*

accel.

Ta - ges wil - der Drang; grell und täu - - schend sein Ge -
day's mad rush ap - pear. Bright and bale - - ful - ly its

p *sf* *più f* *p* *accel.*

stirn_____ weckt zu Trug und Wahn_____ mir das
eyes_____ wake my brain to fol - - ly and

p *p cresc.* - - - - -

T. Hirn!
lies!

Ver
Ac -

più f

riten. *accel.* *riten.*

fluch - - - ter Tag mit dei - nem Schein!
curs - - - ed day, this glare of thine

riten. *accel.* *riten.*

f *fp* *cresc.* *f*

accel. **Sehr bewegt. Molto mosso.**

Wachst du e - - - - - wig mei - ner
wak - ens aye_____ this grief of

accel.

fp *cresc.* *ff* *ff trem.*

Pein? Brennt___ sie e - - wig, die - se Leuch -
mine. Must___ that torch___ be ev - er burn - -

dim.

Sehr allmählich langsamer werdend. Poco a poco ritardando.
(Allmählich abnehmend.) (Poco a poco calando.)

- - te, die selbst Nachts von ihr mich scheuch - te? Ach, I
- - ing, that by night e'en was my warn - ing? Ah! thou

p

sol - - de, sü - - sse Hol - de!
fair - - est, sweet - - est, rar - - est!

Wann end - lich, wann, ach wann lö - schest du die
When, dear - est, when, ah! when wilt thou quench its

Immer ruhiger.
Sempre più tranquillo. (more and more faintly)

Zün - de, dass sie mein Glück mir kün - de?
burn - ing, that it may end my yearn - ing?

(He sinks back gently, exhausted.)

Das Licht, wann löscht es aus?
The light,— when dies that spark!

Wann wird es Ruh' im Haus?
When will the house be dark?

Mässig beginnend und schnell bewegter.
Moderato cominciando e poi stringendo subito.

Kurvenal (after great distress, quickly rousing himself from his dejection)

Der einst ich trotzt,' aus Treu' zu dir, mit dir nach ihr nun muss ich mich seh nen. Glaub' meinem Wort: du sollst sie se-hen, hier und heut'; den Trost kann ich dir ge-ben, ist sie nur selbst noch am Le-ben.

For her who once, for faith to thee, was feared by me, with thee am I long ing. Take thou my word: for thou shalt see her, here, to-day: That hope's still in my giv-ing, so she her-self still be liv-ing.

rallent.

18325

Langsamer. Più lento.

Tristan (very faintly)

Noch losch das Licht nicht aus, / noch ward's nicht Nacht im
Still shines the torch's spark, / still is the house not

Haus: I - sol - de lebt und wacht; sie rief mich aus der Nacht.
dark: I - sol - da lives a - right; she called me from the night.

Schnell belebend.
Stringendo subito.

Kurvenal.

Lebt___ sie denn, so lass dir Hoff - - nung
Lives___ she still, then let that hope___ sus -

la-chen! Muss Kur-we-nal dumm dir gel - ten, heut'___
tain thee! Eh, Kur-ve-nal! fool you hold me, this___

___ sollst du ihn nicht schel - - - ten.
___ day thou shalt not scold me.

Wie todt
As dead

lagst du seit dem Tag, da Me-lot, der Ver-ruch - te, dir ei - ne
layst thou since the day when Me-lot, the ac-curs - ed, dealt thee a

Wun-de schlug. Die bö - se Wun - de, wie sie
griev-ous wound. How should I heal thee, sore-ly

hei - len? Mir thör'-gem Man - ne dünkt'es da, wer
wound-ed? Thy hum-ble ser - vant had the thought that

einst dir Mo-rold's Wun - de schloss, der
she, who Mo-rold's wounds did heal, of

18325

K.

heil - te leicht die Pla - - gen, von Me - lot's Wehr ge-
those could light - ly heal____ thee, that Me - lot's sword did

K.

schla - gen. Die be - ste Ärz - - -
deal thee. Thy best phy - si - - -

ausdrucksvoll
espressivo

K.

- tin bald ich fand; nach Korn - wall
- cian will she be; to Corn - wall

cresc.

K.

hab' ich aus - ge - sandt: ein treu -
has been sent by me a trust -

K.

- er Mann wohl ü-ber's Meer bringt dir I - sol - den
- y man, who o'er the sea bring-eth I-sold' to

accel.

accel.

f

f *f* *f*

Sehr lebhaft.
Molto vivace.

Tristan (transported)

her.
thee.

I - sol - - - de kommt!
I - sol - - - da comes!

ff

I - sol - - - de naht!
I - sol - - - da here!

(He struggles to find words)

più f

ff

Treu - - - - - - - - e!
Loy - - - - - - - - al- ty!

ff

poco rit.   *a tempo*

Heh - - re, hol - de Treu - - e!
Pure ___ and per - fect loy - - al - ty!

ff   *poco rit.*   *dim.*   *p*   *a tempo*

(He draws Kurvenal towards him and embraces him)
(*sehr feurig*)
(*con molto fuoco*)

molto cresc.   *f*

Von hier an das Zeitmass etwas mässiger als Anfangs.
Da qui il tempo poco più moderato che nel cominciamento.

Mein Kur - wenal, du trau - - ter ___
O Kur - venal, my trust - - y ___

f   *mf*

Freund! ___ Du Treu - er oh - ne Wan - - ken, wie
friend! ___ And true, ___ for ne'er yet shrank ___ ye; how ___

f   *fp*   *fp*   *cresc.* -

Etwas breit.
Poco largamente.

soll dir Tri - stan dan - ken? Mein Schild, mein
now shall Tris - tan thank ye? My guard and

f

T.
Schirm in Kampf und Streit, zu Lust und Leid mir stets be-
shield in war and strife, and aye at hand in joy or
p
f
dim.
reit: Wen ich ge - hasst, den hass-test
grief: Whom I did hate, thou hat-edst,
p
cresc.
f
poco riten.
accel.
du; wen ich ge - minnt, den minn-test
too, whom I have loved, thou lov-edst,
accel.
dim.
p
più p
poco riten.
cresc.
a tempo
du. Dem gu - ten Mar - ke, dient' ich ihm hold,
too. While good king Mark my ser-vice did hold,
a tempo
ff
p
wie warst du ihm treu - er als
thou wert to him tru - er than
dolce
p
Ped.
*
Ped.
*
Ped.
*

Gold! _____
gold! _____

cresc.

ff

Red.   ✲

poco riten.   a tempo

Musst' ich ver-ra-then den ed-len Herrn, wie be-trogst du ihn da so gern!
When I be-trayed him, my no-ble lord, then how will-ing was thine ac-cord!

poco riten.   a tempo

p   p   f

Noch beschleunigend.
Sempre stringendo.

Dir   nicht _____ ei-gen,   ein - zig _____ mein,
Thine   thou _____ art not,   mine   a - lone;

cresc.   più f

Sehr zurückhaltend.   Noch gedehnter.
Molto ritenuto.   Più allargando.

mit   lei-dest du,   wenn ich lei - de: nur   was   ich
thou   suf-frest too, when I suf - fer: save, when   I

ausdrucksvoll und sehr gehalten
ff espressivo e ben tenuto

Weniger gedehnt.
Meno largo.

lei - - - de,   das   kannst du   nicht
suf - - - fer,   then   thou canst   not

dim.

p

18325

Lebhaft (doch nicht zu schnell beginnend).
Vivace (ma non cominciando troppo presto).

lei - den!
bear it!
Dies furcht - - ba - re
These ter - - ri - ble

Seh - - nen, das mich sehrt; dies schmach - ten - de
long - - ings that me_ tear_ these burn - ings of

cresc. poco a poco

Bren - - nen, das mich zehrt; wollt' ich dir's
an - - guish that me sear_ should I re-

nen - - nen, könn - test du's ken - - nen:
veal them, couldst thou but feel them,

Allmählich immer mehr beschleunigend.
Poco a poco sempre più stringendo.

nicht hier wür - dest du wei - len, zur War - - te müss-test du
not here hadst thou re - main - ed, the watch - - tower wouldst thou have

244

ei - len,   mit al - len Sin - nen seh - nend von hinnen, nach
gain - ed,   with ev-'ry sense, too, strain-ing from thence to the

dor - ten trach - ten und spä - hen,   wo ih - re   Se - gel sich blä - hen,
o - cean stretch-ing and peer-ing,   where now her   ship___ must be steer-ing,

wo vor den Win - den,   mich zu fin - den,   von der Lie   be
with winds be-hind   her,   me to find   her,   while the fire   of

Drang   be - feu - ert,   I - sol -
love   up - cheer - eth,   I - sol -

- de zu mir   steu - ert!   I - sol -
- da to me   steer - eth!

più f   ff

18325

Es naht! Es naht mit mu- -thiger Hast!
She comes! She comes! with mas- -terful speed!

Sie weht, sie weht, die Flag- ge am Mast!
It waves! It waves! the flag___ at mast-head!

Das Schiff! Das Schiff! Dort streicht es am
The Ship! The Ship! She makes by the

Riff! Siehst du es nicht?
rip! Dost thou not see?

(heftig) (con impeto)

Kurwenal! Siehst_ du es nicht?
Kur-venal! Dost__ thou not see?

8325

Mässig langsam.
Lento moderato.

(As Kurvenal hesitates to leave Tristan, who gazes at him in mute expectation, the mournful tune of the shepherd is heard, as at the beginning)

p

(Cor anglais on the stage.)

f

Kurvenal (dejectedly)

Noch___ ist kein Schiff zu
Still___ there's no ship in

ff *p*

seh'n!
sight!

p

p *f* *dim.*

(Tristan has listened with waning excitement and now begins, with growing melancholy)

p *sf*

Tristan.

Muss ich dich so versteh'n, du al - te,
Must I so take thee, then, old tune so

p

ern- ste Wei- se, mit dei- ner Kla- ge Klang?
sad and sol- emn, with all thy weight of woe?

Durch A- bend-
On eve- ning

we- hen drang sie bang, als einst dem Kind des
air didst drang sad- ly blow, to tell the child his

Va- ters Tod ver- kün- det;
fa- ther's death be- fall- en;

durch Mor- gen- grau- en bang und
through morn- ing's twi- light, drear and

Sehr zurückhaltend.
Molto ritenuto.

T.

bän- ger, als der Sohn der Mut-ter Los _____ ver- nahm.
drear- er, when the son his mother's fate _____ was told.

dim. *più* *p*

Etwas weniger zurückgehalten.
Poco meno ritenuto.

Erstes Zeitmass.
Tempo primo.

T.

Da er mich zeugt' und starb, sie ster-bend mich ge- bar,
When he who sired me died, she died as I was born.

pp *p* *p*

T.

die al - te Wei - se sehn- _____ - sucht - bang zu
The old, old song to them, _____ as well, brought

cresc. *f* *dim.* *più* *p*

T.

ih - nen wohl auch kla- -gend drang, die einst mich
sor- row, too, and for- -tune fell, that asked me

p *p* *sf* *p*

T.

frug, und jetzt mich frägt: zu wel - chem Los er - ko - ren, ich
then, and asks me now: What fate did life al - lot me, when

sf *p*

accel.

T. da - mals wohl ge - bo - ren? Zu welchem Los? _____
it that day be - got me? What is my fate? _____

sf p accel. sf dim.

T. Die al - te Wei - se sagt mir's wie - der:
(Cor anglais on the stage.) That an - cient strain a - gain would tell me: _

p f dim.

T. mich seh - nen _ und ster _ -
In yearn - ing to per -

p f dim. _ - - -

c. ben! Nein! ach nein! _ So _ heisst sie
ish! Nay! Ah nay! _ It _ means not

p sehr gehalten
f molto tenuto

nicht! Seh - nen!
that! Long - ing!

più f

Etwas beschleunigend.
Poco stringendo.

Seh- -nen! Im Ster-ben mich zu seh- -nen, vor
Long- -ing! To die while I am long- -ing, yet

Wieder ruhiger, wie zuvor.
Più tranquillo, come prima.

Sehn-sucht nicht _____ zu ster-ben!
live for ver- _____ -y long-ing.

(Cor anglais on the stage.)

Die nie er-stirbt, seh- -nend nun ruft um
What di-eth not, lov- -ing-ly calls, my

Ster- bens Ruh' ___ sie der fer-nen Ärz- tin zu.__
death to ease, ___ my I-sol-da o'er ___ the seas.

ausdrucksvoll
espressivo

morendo

Sterbend lag ich stumm im
Dying and a drift I

Kahn, der Wunde Gift dem Her-zen nah':
lay, the venom'd wound was near my heart:

Sehn-
wist-

-sucht kla-gend klang die Wei-se; den Se-gel bläh-te der
-ful wailed that strain of sor-row; the winds our cours-es be-

Wind hin zu Ir-lands Kind.
guiled, far to Ire-land's child.

Die Wun-de, die sie hei-lend
The wound that she had closed and

18325

T.
schloss, riss mit dem Schwert sie wieder los; das
healed, she with the sword a-gain re-vealed, that
cresc.
f
Schwert dann a-ber liess sie sin-ken; den
sword then let she fall to save me; un-
p
p f
Gift-trank gab sie mir zu trin-ken: wie ich da
til the poi-soned draught she gave me; and when there-
p f
p f
hoff-te ganz zu ge-ne-sen, da war der seh-rendste
with I hoped to re-store me, I found a fe-ver-ing
pp
cresc.
f
Zau-ber er-le-sen: dass nie ich soll-te
ma-gic was o'er me, that death would find me
ff
p
p

T.
ster- - ben, mich ew'- - ger Qual ver-
nev- - er, but life in pain for
er- - ben!
ev- - er!
più f
Der Trank! der Trank! der furcht-ba-re Trank!
That draught! that draught! that ter-ri-ble draught!
ff
ffp
Wie vom Herz zum Hirn er wü - thend mir drang!
How from breast to brain I burned as I quaff'd!
dim.
cresc.
Kein Heil nun kann, kein sü - sser Tod je
No care can cure, no death re-gain for

T.

_ mich be-frei'n ___ von der Sehn- -sucht Noth, ___
_ me my free- -dom from wist- -ful pain; ___

fp *fp* *fp*

T.

nir- -gends, ach nirgends find' ich Ruh': mich wirft die
no- -where, ah no-where is there rest; for I'm by

fp *cresc.* *f*

T.

Nacht dem Ta - ge zu um e- -wig an mei-nen
night to day-light cast, for aye while my woe doth

f *più f* *ff*

poco rall. *a tempo* (Etwas schleppend.)
(Poco strascinante.)

T.

Lei - den der Son - ne Au - ge zu wei-den. O die-ser
wound me, the sun-light shin - eth a-round me! O yon-der

poco rall. *a tempo*
sf dim. *p* *p* *f* *p* *f*
sf *sf*

T.

Son - ne sen-gender Strahl, wie brennt mir das Hirn sei-ne glü - hen-de
sun-light's with-er-ing beam, it burn - eth my brain with the glow of its

p *f* *p* *molto cresc.*

sf

T. Qual!_____ Für die - ser Hit- -ze heis - sses Ver-
gleam!_____ This hate - ful heat doth with- er and

immer
sempre **f**

T. schmach - ten, ach, kei - nes Schat - - tens küh - lend Um -
burn me_ no shad- ows cool where- to I can

T. nach- - ten! Für die - ser Schmer - zen schreck - li - che
turn _____ me! Of this deep ache, this an - guish of

Pein, welcher Bal - sam soll - te mir Lind'- rung verleih'n? Den furcht-baren
pain, nev-er bal - sam's vir-tue will heal me a-gain! The ter - ri-ble

p _____ **f** **p** *molto cresc._

Trank, der der Qual mich ver-traut, ich selbst,____
draught, that my life has in-dued with pain,____

ff *p cresc.*

Gedehnt.
Steso.

ich selbst, ____ ich hab' ihn ge-braut!
by me, ____ by me was it brew'd!

ff *ff*
f

Aus Va--ters Noth und Mut--ter-Weh',
Of fa--ther's grief, of moth--er's cry,

dim. *p* *ff*

aus Lie-bes-thrä-nen eh' und je, aus
of lov-ers' tears from aye and aye, from

dim. *p* *ff*

Etwas drängender.
Poco più stringendo.

La-chen und Wei-nen, Won-nen und Wun-
joy and from wounds,____ laugh-ter and sor- -

p molto cresc.

18325

T.
den hab' ich des Tran-kes Gif - te ge-
row, Did I that po-tion's poi - son
più f
fun - den! Den ich ge-braut, der mir ge-flos-
bor - row! Such was my brew, such to me slipped
ff
dim.
p
sen, den Won - ne schlürfend je ich ge-
it, Such filled with rap-ture ev-er I
ff
dim.
p
Ped.
nos - sen, ver-
sipped it; I
più f
Ped.
Breiter. Più largo.
flucht sei, furcht - ba-rer Trank!
curse thee, hor - ri-ble draught!
ff
dim.

T. Ver-flucht, wer dich ge-
Cursed he, that brewed and

ausdrucksvoll
espressivo

dim.

Schnell und heftig.
Presto con fuoco.
(He sinks back senseless)

T. braut!
quaff'd!

Kurvenal (who has been vainly striving to calm Tristan, cries out in terror)

K. Mein Herre! Tri - stan! Schreck - licher
My master! Tris - tan! Hor - ri - ble

ff *ff*

K. Zau - ber! O Min - - netrug!
ma - gic! O lures of love!

ff *ff* *p* *cresc.*

Zurückhaltend.
Ritenuto.
sehr getragen und gedehnt
molto portato e largamente

K. O Lie - - bes-zwang! Der Welt hol - dester Wahn! Wie ist's um dich ge-
O pas - sion's lash! Of world-dreams, fairest one! What is this thou hast

ff *p cresc.* *ff*

Sehr zurückhaltend.
Molto ritard.

Mässiger.
Più moderato.

than! / Hier liegt er nun, / der wonni-ge Mann, der wie
done! / Here lies he now, / the noblest of men; such a

Etwas lebhafter.
Poco più vivo.

Wieder gedehnter.
Più steso.

Kei-ner ge - liebt und geminnt. / Nun seht, was von ihm sie Dankes ge-
lov-er was nev-er be-fore. / Behold, what re-turn love get-teth a-

Sehr mässig.
Molto moderato.

(his voice broken by sobs)

wann, was je Min - ne'sich ge - winnt! / Bist du nun
gain! 'Tis all love___ wins ev-er - more! / Art thou then

todt? Lebst du noch? / Hat dich der Fluch entführt?
dead? Liv'st thou still? / Hast thou thy fate ful-fill'd?

Mässig langsam.
Lento moderato.

(He listens for his breath)

sehr zart
dolcissimo

18325

O Wonne! Nein! Er regt sich, er lebt!_
O rapture! No! He stir-reth, he lives!_

Wie sanft er die Lippen rührt!
and soft-ly his lips he moves.

Tristan (beginning very faintly)

Das Schiff?
The ship?

Siehst du's noch
See'st thou it

Kurvenal.

nicht? Das Schiff? Ge-wiss, es naht noch heut': es kann nicht lang'mehr säumen.
yet? The ship? Rest sure,'twill come to-day: 'Twill not de-lay much longer.

mit zunehmendem Ausdruck
con espressione sempre crescente

Tristan.

Und drauf I - sol - de, wie sie winkt,—
It bears I - sol - da, smil-ing, see

wie sie hold mir Süh - - ne trinkt:—
how she par - don drinks———— to me.

Siehst du sie? Siehst du sie noch nicht?
See'st her not? Canst not see her yet?

Sehr ruhig und nicht schleppend.
Molto tranquillo, ma non strascinante.

Wie sie se - lig, hehr und mil - de_
See her, drawn by deep de - vo - tion,

Text underlay (German / English):

wan - delt durch des Meer's Ge - fil - de? Auf
has - ten o'er the fields of o - cean? O'er

won - - ni - ger Blu - men lich - ten Wo - gen kommt sie
flow - - er - y bil - lows fleet - ly far - ing, gen - tly

sanft ans Land ge - zo - - gen.
now the land she's near - - ing.

Sie lä - -
She smiles

-chelt mir Trost und sü - - sse
to me rest, and per - fect

Etwas breit.
Poco largamente.

18325

T.
Ruh', sie führt mir letz - te La - bung zu.
peace, at last she brings me my re - lease.
poco
più p
p dolce
cresc.
f
dim.
p
Ach, I - sol - - - de! I -
Ah, I - sol - - - - da! I -
p dolce
cresc.
f
dim.
Immer breiter.
Sempre più largamente.
Breit.
Largamente.
sol - de! Wie schön bist
sol - da! How fair art
p
più p
Lebhafter.
Più vivo.
du! Und Kur - wenal,
thou! And Kur - venal,
p
(staccato, ma ben tenuto)
p

T.
wie, du säh'st sie nicht? Hinauf zur War - te, du blöder
thou, thou saw'st her not? A-way to the watch-tow'r, thou laz-y
poco cresc.
Wicht! Was so hell und licht ich se - he, dass das dir nicht ent -
lout! So, if I so clear - ly mind her, do not thou fail to
p
Allmählich immer mehr belebend.
Sempre poco a poco animando.
ge - he! Hörst du mich nicht? Zur War - te schnell! Ei - lig zur
find her! Dost thou not hear? To watch a-way! Haste to the
ausdrucksvoll
p espressivo
ben marcato
cresc.
War - te! Bist du zur Stell'? Das Schiff? das Schiff? I - sol -
watch - tow'r! Why dost thou stay? The ship! the ship! I - sol -
f
p
cresc.
- - den's Schiff? Du musst es se - hen! Musst
- - da's ship! Thou hast to see it! Hast
f

es se - hen!
to see it!

Das Schiff?
The ship!

(Whilst Kurvenal, still hesitating, opposes Tristan,
the shepherd's pipe is heard without)

Säh'st du's noch nicht?
See'st it not yet?

trem.

(Cor anglais on the stage.)

Kurvenal (springing joyously up)

O Won - - - ne!
Thank heav - - - en!

Sehr lebhaft.
Molto vivace.

Freu - - - - de!
Thank heaven!

(Cor anglais on the stage.)

18325

266

(He rushes to the watch-tower and looks out.)

Kurvenal (breathlessly)

Ha! das
Ha! the

Schiff! Von Nor-den seh'ich's na - - hen.
ship! From northward it is near - - ing.

p *molto cresc.* - - - - -

Tristan.

Wusst'___ ich's nicht? Sagt'___ ich's nicht? dass sie noch lebt,
Knew___ I not? what___ said I! That she still lives,

ff *dim.* - - - - *pp cresc.* - - -

___ noch Le - - ben mir webt?___ Die mir I - sol - - de
___ and life___ for me weaves!___ Naught but I - sold' ___ the

f *f*

18325

ein - - zig ent - hält, wie wär' I - sol - de mir aus der
world__ holds for me, how could I - sold' in my world not

Welt!
be!

Kurvenal (shouting)

(Cor anglais on the stage.)

Hei - ha! Hei - ha!
A - hoy! A - hoy!

Wie es mu - thig steu - ert! Wie stark der Se - gel sich bläht! Wie es
see her brave - ly sail - ing! The sails, how fine - ly_ they draw! How she

(Orchestra)

Tristan.

jagt, wie es fliegt! Die Flag - ge? Die Flag - ge?
forg - es and flies! The pen - nant! The pen - nant!

sempre stacc.

Kurvenal.

Der Freu - - de Flag - ge am Wim - pel
The ga - - la flags at the mast - head,

cresc. poco a

lu - stig und hell! Ha - hei, der Freu - de! Hell am Ta - ge zu
joy - ful and gay! A - ha! Here's joy now! Comes by day - light to

Tristan.

poco

mir I - sol - de! I - sol -
me, I - sol - da, I - sol -

più f

de zu mir! I - sol -
da! to me! I - sol

ff

Kurvenal.

Siehst du sie selbst? Jetzt schwand das Schiff
See'st her, her - self? Just now the ship's

meno f *dim.*

Tristan.

hin - ter dem Fels. Hinter dem Riff? Bringt es Ge -
hid by the rocks. Behind the reef? Is aught to

p

Noch schneller.
Più presto.

T.

fahr?
fear?

Dort wü - thet die Brandung,
The wa - ter aye breaks there!

ff *f* *ff*

Kurv.

T.
K.

schei-tern die Schif-fe!
ships have been shattered!

Das Steu - er, wer führt's? Der
And who's at the helm? The

f

Tristan.

K.
T.

si - cherste See - mann. Ver-rieth___ er mich?
sur-est of sea - men. One true___ to me?

Wär' er Me-lot's Ge-
Not of Me-lot's em-

ff *ff* *ff* *ff*

Kurvenal.
Tristan.

T.
K.
T.

noss?
ploy?

Trau' ihm wie mir!
Trust him like me!

Ver - rä - - - ther auch
Thou treach - - - er-ous,

sempre più ff

T.

du!
too!

Un - sel' - ger!
Thou vil - lain!

ff *ff*

Noch mehr beschleunigend.
Ancora più accel.

Kurvenal.

Siehst du sie wie - der?
Dost thou yet see her?

Noch
Not

nicht.
yet.

Tristan.

Ver - lo - ren!
She's lost, then!

Früheres Zeitmass.
Tempo primo.

Kurvenal (shouting)

Hei - ha! Heiha - ha - ha!
A-hoy! a-hoy! a - hoy!

(Cor anglais on the stage.)

Tristan (shouting)

Vor - bei! Vor - bei! Glück - lich vor - bei!
They're by! They cleared safe - ly! They're by!

Heiha - ha - ha!
A-hoy! a - hoy!

(Orchestra)

cresc.

Kur - - we - nal, treu -
Kur - - ve - nal, faith -

18325

T.
-e-ster Freund! ____ All' mein Hab' ____
-ful-lest friend! ____ All my goods ____

ff　　　　　　　　　　　　　　*poco dim.*

T.
_____ und Gut _____ ver-erb' ich noch heu -
_____ and gold _____ to-day I do give

più dim.　　　*p*

Kurvenal.　　　**Tristan.**

T.
K.
te. Sie na-hen im Flug. Siehst du sie end-lich? Siehst du I -
thee. She comes like the wind! Now canst thou see her? See'st thou I -

poco cresc.

Kurvenal.

T.
K.
sol - de? Sie ist's! Sie winkt!
sol - da? 'Tis she! She waves!

f　　　*p*　　　*f*

Tristan.

T.
O se - - lig-stes Weib!
O wo - - man di-vine!

p　　*cresc.*　　*f*

272

Kurvenal.

Im Ha - - fen der Kiel!
In har - - bour's the ship!

I - sol - de, ha! mit ei - nem Sprung springt sie vom
I - sol - da! Ha! a sin - gle spring brings her from

Immer beschleunigend.
Sempre accelerando.

Tristan.

Bord ans Land. Her - ab von der War - te, mü - ssiger Gaffer! Hin-
ship to shore! A - way from the watch-tow'r, stop i-dly staring! A-

Kurvenal.

ab! Hin - ab an den Strand! Hilf ihr! Hilf meiner Frau! Sie trag'ich her-
way! anddown to the shore! Help her! Help la - dy mine! Safe and sound in my

poco riten.   accel.

auf: trau' meinen Armen! Doch du, Tristan, bleib mir treulich am Bett!
arms light-ly I'll bear her! But thou, Tristan, keepthee well on thy couch!

poco riten.   accel.

18325

Scene II.

Sehr lebhaft.
Molto vivace.

(Kurvenal hastens away. — Tristan tosses on his couch in extreme excitement)

Tristan.

O_____ die-se Sonne!
O_____ sun that pourest!

Ha! dieser Tag! Ha dieser Won - ne son - nigster
Glo - rious ray! Joy thou re - stor - est, sun - ni - est

Tag! Ja - gendes Blut, jauch - zen - der
day! Cours - es my blood, grows my heart

Muth! Lust oh - ne Ma - ssen, freu -
good! Joy without mea - sure! Fren -

18325

T. accel.

-di-ges Ra - sen! Auf des La - gers Bann, wie___ sie er-
-zy of plea - sure! *accel.* Can I brook to stay, this___ sick-bed

tra - gen! Wohlauf___ und dar-an, wo die Her-zen schla - gen!
keep - ing! Nay! Up___ and a-way, to where hearts are leap - ing!

Tri - stan, der Held, in ju - beln-der Kraft,___ hat sich vom
Tris-tan, the knight, with glo - ri - ous pow'r___ has snatch'd him-

(He raises himself quite up)

Tod em - por - ge - rafft. Mit blu - ten der Wun-de be-
self from death once more! Once blood - y and wounded Sir

kämpft' ich einst Mo - rol - den: mit
Mo - rold I en - coun - terd: Now

(He tears the bandage from his wound)

(He springs from his bed and staggers forward)

blu - - - - - - ten-der Wun-de er jag' ich mir
blood - - - - - - y and wound-ed I - sol - da shall

heut' I - sol - den! Hei-a, mein Blut!
be con - front - ed! A - ha! my blood!

lu - stig nun flie - sse! Die mir die Wun - de
Gai - ly it flows now! She that this wound of

e - wig schlie-sse, sie naht wie ein Held, sie naht mir zum Heil! Ver-
mine can close now; she comes like a queen to heal me at need, the

geh' die Welt mei-ner jauch-zenden Eil'!
world, I ween, must make way to her speed!

18325

(He totters to the centre of the stage)

Isolda (without)

Tri -
Tris -

più f   *ff trem.*   *dim.*

- stan! Ge-lieb - - ter!   Wie, hör' ich das Licht? die Leuch-te, ha!
- tan! Be-lov - - ed!   What, hear I the light? the torch-light, ah!

Tristan (in frantic excitement)

p

Die Leuch - te ver-lischt! Zu ihr!   Zu
The light is gone out! I come!   To

f   *p*   *molto cresc.*

Isolda hastens breathlessly in. Tristan, out of his senses, staggers weakly towards her.
They meet in the centre of the stage; she receives him in her arms)

ihr!
her!

ff sempre

3 3   *Red.*

Sehr allmählig nachlassend im Zeitmass. Poco a poco allargando.

ff   *ff*

3 3   *Red.*   *Red.*

Isolda. (Tristan sinks slowly to the ground in Isolda's arms)

Tri - - - stan!
Tris - - - tan!

dim.

Ha!
Ah!

sehr ausdrucksvoll
molto espressivo

Sehr langsam.
Adagio.

p

più p

Tristan (raising his eyes to Isolda, as he dies)

Isolda.

Bewegt.
Animato.

I - sol - de!   (He dies)   Ha!   Ich bin's,   ich
I - sol - da!   Ha!   'Tis I,   'tis

dolce più p

pp

p

Etwas zurückhaltend.
Poco ritenuto.

accel.

bin's,   sü - sse - ster Freund! Auf, noch einmal hör' mei - nen   Ruf!   I - sol - de
I,   dear - est, my   love! Come, hear once a - gain when I   call!   I - sol - da

accel.

cresc.

f   *ff*

p

Noch mehr zurückhaltend
Più ritenuto.

Mässig langsam.
Lento moderate.

ruft: I - sol - de kam, mit Tri - stan treu zu ster - ben!
calls, I - sol - da's here, to Tris - tan true, to die with him!

Belebter
Piu vivo.

Bleibst du mir stumm? Nur ei - ne Stun - de, nur ei - ne
Wilt thou not speak? On - ly an hour, one single

Belebter.
Animato.

Etwas gedehnt.
Poco stesto.

Stun - de blei-be mir wach!
hour, live thou with me!

molto cresc.
f
sehr ausdrucksvoll
molto espress.
dim.

So ban - ge Ta - ge wach-te sie seh - nend, um ei - ne
The drear-y days I wait-ed in long- -ing, that we might

p
p
cresc.

Mässig langsam.
Lento moderato.

rallent.

Stun - de mit dir noch zu wa - chen. Betrügt I - solden, betrügt sie
live on-ly one hour to-geth - er! Deceived I - sol-da? Be-reft by

rallent.
espressivo
più p
cresc.

3

Belebend.
Animando.

Tri-stan um die-ses ein - zi-ge, e - wig kur - - ze,
Trís-tan of e'en this sin - -gle so short, so lit - - tle,

f dim.

Zurückhaltend.
Rallent.

Sehr zurückhaltend. Bewegter.
Molto ritenuto. Più animato.

letz - - - te Wel-ten-glück? Die Wunde? Wo?
last — of earth-ly joy? Art wounded?Where?

p   *più p*   *p*

Lass_ sie mich hei - len! Dass won - - - -
I'll_ heal thee, dear-est! Till rap - - - -

cresc.   *f*   *p dolce*   *p*

- nig und hehr die Nacht wir thei - len, nicht_ an der
- ture of night with me _ thou shar - est! Die_ not of

p   *mf*   *p*

Wun - - de, an der Wun-de stirb' mir nicht: uns Bei - den ver -
wounds, not of the wounds re - ceived in strife! For both, as if

Sehr zurückhaltend
Molto ritenuto.

eint er - lö - sche das Le - - - bens-licht!
one, ex - tin - guish the light of life!

sehr ausdrucksvoll
molto espressivo

Gebrochen der Blick! Still das Herz!
All glassy his glance! Still his heart!

Nicht ei - nes A - - thems flücht'ges Weh'n!
Hast not one fleet - ing breath for me?

sehr ausdrucksvoll
molto espressivo

Bewegter.
Più mosso.

accel.

Muss sie nun jam — mernd vor dir steh'n, die sich
Leav'st me im — plor — ing here by thee? I, that

Immer bewegter.
Sempre più mosso.

won — nig dir zu ver — mäh — len mu — thig kam über's
joy — ous, will-ing to wed thee, brave — ly sail'd o'er the

Heftig bewegt.
Molto animato.

Meer? Zu spät!__ Trot — zi — ger
sea? Too late!__ Cru — el — lest

immer
sempre ff

Mann! Strafst__ du mich so mit här — te-stem
love! Pun — ish-ment this, all an — guish a —

Immer heftiger.
Sempre string.

Bann? Ganz____ oh — ne Huld mei — ner Lei — dens —
bove! No____ pit — y thine for this grief of

Allmählich wieder nachlassend.
Poco a poco calando.

rall. poco

schuld?   Nicht mei - ne Kla - gen darf ich dir sa - gen?
mine?   Hast speech for - bid - den? Must they be hid - den?

Nur ein - mal, ach! nur ein - mal noch!
But once more, ah! but once a - gain!

Immer langsamer.
Sempre ritard.

Tri - stan!   Ha!
Tris - tan!   Ah!

Langsam.
Lento.

horch!   Er wacht!   Ge -
hark!   He wakes!   Be -

(She sinks down senseless upon his body)

lieb - ter!
lov - ed!

18325

Scene III.

(Kurvenal had entered immediatly after Isolda; in speechless horror, he has remained near the entrance gazing motionless on Tristan. From below is now heard the dull tumult of voices and clash of weapons. The Shepherd climbs over the wall)

Lebhaft bewegt.
Allegro animato.

The Shepherd (coming quickly and softly to Kurvenal)

Kur-we-nal! Hör'!
Kur- ve-nal! Hear!

(Kurvenal starts up in haste and looks over the rampart, whilst the Shepherd stands apart gazing in consternation on Tristan and Isolda)

Ein zwei - tes Schiff!
An - oth - er ship!

Kurvenal. **Noch lebhafter.** (angrily)
Più vivo.

Tod und Höl-le!   Al-les zur Hand!   Mar - ke und
Death's de-struction!   Ready, my men!   Me - lot and

Me - lot hab'ich er-kannt.   Waffen und Steine!   Hilf mir! Ans Thor!
Mark, they are to my ken!   Weapons and boulders! Help! to the gate!

18325

(He hurries with the shepherd to the gate, which they hastily try to barricade)

The Helmsman (rushes in)

Mar - ke mir nach mit Mann und Volk: ver-geb'- ne Wehr, be-
Mark with his men are af - ter me: in vain we warred, for

Kurvenal.

wäl-tigt sind wir. Stell' dich, und hilf!
worsted are we! Stand by and help!

So lang' ich le - - - be, lugt mir Kei - ner her-
While life doth last, I let none en - ter a-

Brangæna (without, calling from below)   **Kurvenal.**

ein! I - sol - de! Her - rin! Bran - gä - nen's Ruf?
live! I - sol - da! Mis - tress! Bran - gæ - na's voice?

p   *cresc.*

(calling down)   **Brangæna.**

Was suchst du hier? Schliess' nicht, Kur-we-nal!   Wo ist I - sol - de?
What dost thou here? O - pen, Kur-ve-nal!   Where is I - sol - da?

fp   *p*   *cresc.*

Kurvenal.   **Melot** (without)

Ver-räth'rin auch du? Weh' dir, Ver-ruch-te! Zu-rück, du Thor! Stemm'dich nicht
Betray'st thou them too? Woe to thee, faith-less! Stand back, thou fool! Make way, I

f   *f*

Wild.   **Kurvenal** (laughing savagely)
Furioso.

dort!   Hei - a-ha - ha!   Dem
say!   Ah! it has come,   this

ff   *ff*

Tag, _____ an dem ich dich tref - - fe!
day! _____ on which I can strike thee!

18325

(Melot with armed men appears under the gateway. Kurvenal rushes upon him and strikes him down)
K.
Stirb', schändli-cher Wicht!
Die, in - fa-mous wretch!
ff
f p mf cresc.
Ped. *
Melot.
Me.
Weh mir! Tri - stan!
Woe's me! Tris - tan!
f ff f
(He dies)
Brangæna (still without)
Kurvenal.
B.
K.
Kur-we-nal! Wü - then-der! Hör', du be-trügst dich! Treu-lo-se
Kur-ve-nal! Hear me! Art mad? Thou mis-tak'st us! Treacher-ous
ff p f p cresc.
(to his men)
(They fight)
K.
Magd! Drauf! Mir nach! Werft sie zu - rück!
maid! Come! Fol - low! Fling them all back!
ff
Mark.(without)
M.
Hal - te, Ra - sen-der! Bist du von Sin-nen?
Hold, thou ma - ni - ac! Art thou be-side thee?

Kurvenal.

Hier _____ wü _____ thet der
Here _____ rag _____ es but

Tod!
Death!

Nichts And'-res, Kö _____ nig, ist hier zu
Naught else, O King, _____ from here may be

(He sets upon Mark and his followers)

Mark.

ho- len: Willst du ihn kie-sen, so komm! Zu- rück! Wahn -
tak- en: if thou wouldst cull it, then come! Stand back! In -

(Mark appears with his followers under the gate)

- sin - ni - ger!
- sen-sate fool!

(Brangæna has climbed over the wall at side and hastens to the front)

Brangæna.

I-sol - de!   Her - rin!   Glück   und
I-sol - da!   Mis - tress!   Give   you

più f

Heil!   Was   seh'   ich!
joy!   What   see   I!

più f

Immer noch beschleunigend.
Sempre più string.

(She devotes herself to Isolda)

Ha!   Lebst   du,   I - sol - de?
Ha!   Liv'st   thou,   I - sol - da?

_ff_

Mark(who with his followers has driven Kurvenal and his assistants back from the gate and forced his way in)

O   Trug   und Wahn!   Tri -
O   ly - -ing dream!   Tris -

più f

Langsamer.
Più lento.

(Kurvenal, deeply wounded, totters before Mark towards the front)

Kurvenal.

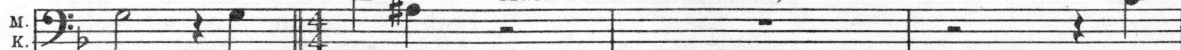

stan! Wo bist du?
tan! Where art thou?

Da
Here

ff

dim. - - -

Sehr zurückhaltend.
Molto ritenuto.

He sinks down at Tristan's feet) **Mark.**

liegt er, hier, wo ich lie-ge.
lies he, here, where I lay me.

Tri-stan! Tri - stan! I - sol - - de!
Tris-tan! Tris - tan! I - sol - - da!

p *ausdrucksvoll espressivo*

dim.

Langsam.
Lento.

Kurvenal (clutching at Tristan's hand)

Weh! Tri - stan! Trau - ter! Schilt mich nicht,
Woe! Tris - - tan! Mas - ter! Chide him not,

più p *espress.*
pp

e più p

Noch mehr zurückhaltend.
Ancora più ritenuto.

(He dies)

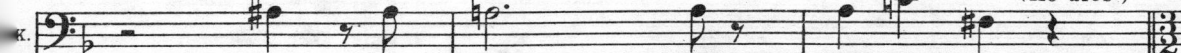

dass der Treu - man - - e auch mit kommt!
if thy man - - would go with thee!

p

più p

18325

Mässig.
Moderato.
Mark.
M.
Todt denn Al - les!
All are dead, then!
pp
p espress.
poco cresc.
Bewegter.
Più animato.
Al - - les todt!
All are dead!
sehr ausdrucksvoll Mein Held, mein
molto espress. My Prince, my
p poco a poco cresc.
Tri - stan! Trau - tester Freund, auch heu-te noch musst du den Freund ver-
Tris - tan! Trust - i-est friend, yet thou this day once more thy friend be-
f
Immer belebter.
Sempre più animato.
ra-then? Heut', wo er kommt dir höch-ste Treu-e zu be-wäh - ren? Er -
tray-est! Now, when he comes, his per-fect trust in thee to prove thee? A -
p
cresc.
più cresc.
wa - che! Er - wa - che! Erwa - che mei - nem
wak - en! A - wak - en! A-wake and hear my
molto cresc.
più f

Zurückhaltend.
Rallentando.
(Bending down sobbing over the bodies)

M. Jam — — mer!
sor — — row!

Du treu - los
Thou faith - less, —

ff *dim.* **p**

M. treu — — ster Freund!
B. faith — — ful friend!

Brangæna (who has revived Isolda in her arms)

Sie wacht, sie lebt! I-
She wakes, she lives! I-

pp **p** **p** **p**

Belebter.
Animando.

B. sol — de! hör' mich,   vernimm mei - ne   Süh — ne!   Des Tran-kes Ge -
sol - da! hear me!   Accept   my a-   -tone-ment!   The draught and   its

p

B. heim-niss   ent-deckt' ich dem   Kö - nig: mit sor - gen - der
se - cret,   I told the King   of it: All anx - ious, with

p   *poco cresc.* — — —   3

B. Eil' stach er in See, dich zu er - rei - chen,   dir — zu ent - sa — — gen, dir
speed he put to sea, that he might reach thee,   so — to re - nounce — thee, and

3   3   3

più cresc. — — —   **f**

18325

Mässig bewegt.
Moderato con moto.
Mark.

zu - zu - füh - - ren den Freund!
e'en so give____ thee thy love.

dolce

War - O

dim.

p

p

um, I - sol - de, war - um mir das? Da hell mir ent -
why, I - sol - da, why this to me? When clear - ly I

hüllt, was zu - vor ich nicht fassen konnt', wie se - lig, dass den Freund ich frei von
saw, what be - fore I had failed to grasp, how glad was I to find my friend from

poco cresc.

p

Belebend.
Animando.

Schuld da fand! Dem hol - den Mann____ dich zu ver -
blame was free! Guilt - less was he;____ so, to be -

p

poco cresc.

mäh - - len, mit vol - len Se - geln flog ich dir nach. Doch
troth ye, with flow - ing sails I flew af - ter thee. Too

M.

Un-glü-ckes Un-ge-stüm, wie er-reicht es, wer Frie-den bringt? Die
wild is the course of woe, for the bring-er of joy t'o'er-take! Death's

ff   *f*   *p*   *cresc.*

poco accel.

M.

Ern - te mehrt' ich dem Tod. Der Wahn häuf - - te die
har - vest I did but swell, fresh woe's er - - -ror com-

poco accel.   *più f*   *ff*   *ff*

Allmählig zurückhaltend.
Rallentando poco a poco.

Brangæna.   (Isolda, unconscious of all around her, turns her eyes

M.
B.

Noth!   Hörst du uns nicht? I-sol - de!   Trau-te! Vernimmst du die Treu - e
pel!   Hear'st thou us not? I-sol - da!   Dearest! Mis-tak - est thou not the

p

Sehr mässig beginnend.
Molto moderato cominciare.

Isolda.

with rising inspiration on Tristan's body)   *pp*

B.
I.

nicht?   Mild und lei-se   wie er lä-chelt,
truth?   Fair and gently   he is smiling;

pp   *pp*

wie das Au – ge hold er öff – net, seht ihr, Freunde,
see, his eyes he soft – ly o – pens! See, my friends, ah!

säh't ihr's nicht? Im – mer lich – ter wie ___ er leuch – tet,
see ye not? how he, bright and bright – er burn – ing,

stern – ___ um – strah – let hoch sich hebt?
stream – ___ – ing star – light, heaves him high?

Etwas bewegter.
Poco più animato.

Seht ihr's nicht? Wie das Herz ihm
See ye not how his heart with

sempre con Pedale

I.
mu - thig schwillt, voll und
cour - age swells, strong and
p
hehr im Bu - sen ihm quillt?
pure with - in him it wells?
Wie den Lip - - - pen,
From his lips how
p
p dolce
won - - - nig mild, sü -
soft and sweet comes
p
p dolce

I.

p

-sser A - them sanft ent to
the breath he - breathes to

p dolce

p

I.

weht. Freun - de!
me. Friends, ah!

p

p dolce

I.

Seht! Fühlt und seht ihr's nicht?
see! Feel ye, see ye not?

p

cresc.

I.

Hö - re ich nur die - se Wei - se, die so wun - der - and
Hears none else the mu- -sic yon- der that so soft and

pp

poco cresc.

sempre con Pedale

voll und lei-----se, Won------
full of won-----der, sweet------

-----ne klang end, Al----les
-----ly ring-ing, all____things

sa-gend, mild ver-söh-nend aus__ ihm__
sing--ing, from__ him swell--eth, peace fore-

tö--nend, in mich drin-get, auf sich schwinget, hold er-
tell--eth, round me grow-ing, thro' me flow-ing, trum--pet-

18325

I.
hal - lend um mich klin - - - - - - - -
blasts a - round me blow - - - - - - - -
molto cresc.
- - - - - get?
- - - - - ing?
Hel - - - ler
Blow - - - ing
f
p
schal - - lend, mich um wal - - lend, sind es
clear - - er, grow - ing near - - er, are they
Wel - - len sanf - - ter Lüf - te? Sind es
waves in air of a - zure? Are they

Wol - ken won - - ni-ger Düf - te? Wie sie
waves of per - -fume and plea - sure? How they

schwel - len, mich um - rau - schen, soll ich
heave them, how they near them! Dare I

ath - - men, soll ich lau - - schen? Soll ich
breathe them? Dare I hear them? Shall I

schlür - fen, un - ter - tau - chen, süss in Düf - ten mich ver -
drink them, dive a - mong them, Where in per - fume they have

I.
hau - chen? In dem wo - - - gen-den
flung them? In their bil - - - low-y
Schwall, in dem tö - - - nendem Schall, in des
well, in their res - - o-nant spell, with the
Welt - - - - - - - A - - - - - thems
world's life - - - - - breath,
we - - - - hen - dem All
breath - - - - ing o'er all,
ff
Ped.

I.

er - trin - - ken, ver - sin - - ken,
Sink down ____ in and drown in

dim.

sempre con Pedale

I.

un - - - be - wusst, höch -
dream - - - less rest, high -

più p

- - - ste Lust!
- - est, best!

(Isolda, as if glorified, sinks gently in Bran-

pp

gæna's arms down upon Tristan's body. There is great distress and emotion among the bystanders. Mark

blesses the dead)

morendo   *rallentando*

pp   (The Curtain falls during the final pause)

18325   *Ped.*